Wacky Soap

Script & Lyrics by Mark Wheeller
Music by James Holmes

dbda

Wacky Soap

Script & Lyrics by Mark Wheeller
Music by James Holmes

Author's acknowledgments:

Class 2E (1987) St. John's School, Epping and members of the Epping Youth Theatre 1987.
Alison Burkert, Ryan Gilbey, Jenny Roe and Rachel Wheeller.
Meg Davis, Sophie Gorell Barnes and all at MBA Literary Agency for continued belief and support.
Dawn and Evie at ***dbda*** for their commitment to Wacky Soap.
Geoffrey Greiggs for the wonderful illustrations in the colour storybook.
Ollie, Charlie and Daisy Wheeller for their enthusiastic response to the story as it was being developed.

Originally published as a short story by the Institute of Alcohol Studies (IAS) under the title "Happy Soap".

ISBN 1 902843 02 9

BRITISH LIBRARY CATALOGUING IN PUBLICATION DATA
A catalogue record for this book is available from the British Library.

Published by ***dbda***, Pin Point, 1-2 Rosslyn Crescent, Harrow HA1 2SB.

Further copies of this script can be purchased from:
dbda, Pin Point, 1-2 Rosslyn Crescent, Harrow HA1 2SB.
Tel: 0870 333 7771 Fax: 0870 333 7772 E-mail: orders@dbda.co.uk

Introduction by Mark Wheeller

There have been countless features on the TV asking how substance abuse education can be broached with the very young. I always think that ***Wacky Soap*** can provide an oblique way of approaching this difficult and often controversial subject. It would also serve to remove much of the controversy associated with this issue.

Wacky Soap is an entertaining story. Entertainment is enjoyable and, if you enjoy something, you are willing... even keen to talk about it. Discussion, with careful teacher intervention, is one way to create an environment where effective learning can occur. I am not saying it can stop people from abusing substances, be they cigarettes, alcohol, illegal drugs, butane gas or anything else, but it can raise the issues and provoke an interesting debate because it is looking at the subject from a new perspective.

An allegorical approach enables people of all ages to think freshly about any subject. Allegory has been used in teaching throughout history (check out the teachings of Jesus!). Consider these questions yourself:

- *What would you do if it were announced that Wacky Soap really had been invented?*
- *Would you want to try it?*
- *Would you want to protect your children from it?*
- *Would you let them try it, or turn a blind eye when/if they do?*
- *How do you teach them about the potential dangers... do you talk to them about it or will that in itself bring the product to their attention?*
- *Do you never talk to them so that they remain (blissfully) ignorant of it?*
- *How would you feel if they did (repeatedly or not) temporarily lose a limb (or two)?*
- *Worse still... how would you cope if someone you loved was washed away completely?*
- *Should the government be allowed to make money from it... if so (as in the story) how should that money be spent?*
- *Should the government make it illegal?*

All these serious questions (and many, many more) can be asked of this absurd (or is it?) fictional substance, Wacky Soap. The answers they provoke may, in some cases, cause people to question why they have answered them in the way they have... whereas, when discussing well known substances, everybody arrives with pre-conceptions and feel that they have their opinions set in concrete well before any discussion begins.

I felt that the story did have a future and a place in both the Junior and Secondary school curriculum. I touted it round but with no success... until I showed it to Dawn Boyfield and Evie Efthimiou at ***dbda***. Only a week or so after I had given them the script they wrote to me saying that they wanted to publish a story version, a musical and a cantata for Junior schools! Yes!!!. At last someone else shared my enthusiasm about it!

I certainly hope that the 'rebirth' ***dbda*** are giving to *Wacky Soap* will lead to animated discussions occurring in classrooms across the world and that some schools/theatre groups will choose to present it... both James and I are looking forward to seeing it on stage somewhere... sometime. Good luck to all who attempt to work with or perform this Musical Play. I hope that you will find it both entertaining and challenging to work on.

Postscript – November 2004

Wacky Soap has now become my most successful stage Musical. I regularly get letters from companies saying how much they have enjoyed presenting this and am SO pleased. Teachers say how the involvement of the chorus eases discipline problems in rehearsals! The one change I have chosen to make to the text is something that my Narrator (Jack Duncan) improvised during the Oaklands Youth Theatre production. It occurs just after he has been dismissed by the rebellious chorus – it reminded me of Eric Morecombe walking off at the end of the Morecombe and Wise shows and always elicited a vocal "Ah" from the audience... it appears as a stage instruction just before the final song... so thanks for that Jack!

Since the Musical was originally published, ***dbda*** have also released a wonderful colour story book which provides a great introduction to the musical and offers some great ideas for costumes etc… so do have a look at that… and big thanks to Geoffrey Greiggs for his wonderful illustrations.

One aspect that we had great fun with when presenting it for the first time was the set… we used a Bouncy Castle for the King to deliver his speeches from! One of my friends, Tim Ford, now a director at the Birmingham Rep came to see the production and gave me a wonderful idea which so far no-one has put into action. I hope that someone, somewhere, someday… may be able to. The idea is that Wacky Soap should be presented in a swimming pool... with inflatable props! Wow! What a production that would be… anyone up for that?

Whatever you do… do have fun with it!

Wacky Soap – Birth of a play

Wacky Soap had been published as *Happy Soap* by the IAS (Institute of Alcohol Studies) as a (very) short story in 1987, in an appendix to the initial *Too Much Punch For Judy* publication.

However, the seeds of the story had been sown long before that! Many things make an impression on one as a youngster. For me David Bowie (*Life on Mars* is still my favourite song) and George Best (an unforgettable double hat-trick in Man Utd's 8-2 League Cup thumping of Northampton Town) are at the top of my list.

Then there were television programmes... I can remember tuning in to see the second episode of *Dr Who*, only to discover they repeated the first as so many had missed it due to a power cut! The second was shown immediately afterwards. *Blue Peter* (John Noakes and Shep), *Catweazle* (why doesn't *UK Gold* ever repeat that?) and *Ace of Wands* (with Tarot the 'diamond man' and Lulli), but I suppose the most innovatory of my teen years, was *Monty Python's Flying Circus*. I loved the absurdity of the sketches and the imaginative way they were linked together. The animated films always made me laugh... the woman waiting at a bus stop with busses passing her by, until she sticks out her foot and trips a bus up! It was one of these animations that, subconsciously sowed the seeds, for me, of this story line. It was an irreverent fairy tale with a royal family as the central characters... although they were soon upstaged by a spot from the face of a gawky (and probably very ugly) Prince. I thought it was very, very funny.

In 1986, I was working with the Epping Youth Theatre developing a 'play' on alcohol misuse. This play, ended up becoming a series of sketches, some serious and some funny. The final section was a fifteen minute version of what has since become ***Too Much Punch For Judy***. I wanted something brief to precede it which needed to be humourous, yet thought provoking. It was originally to be an adaptation of a wonderful story by James Thurber entitled *The Bear Who Let It Alone*. On the same day as England lost 1-0 to Portugal in the 1986 World Cup (a few weeks before they finally went out in the quarter finals to Maradonna's 'hand of god' goal), James Thurber's estate wrote refusing us permission to stage his story... I had to think of one myself.

Necessity is the mother of invention. I viewed this problem (only a month before our production date) as an opportunity to come up with something imaginative. One of the group, Ryan Gilbey (now an arts journalist) suggested the idea of a 'Happiness potion'. The idea was that the potion was taken orally, thus making it too close to alcohol itself... but, what if the potion was to be rubbed on the skin?... what if the potion was a soap? These two steps created the forerunner to ***Wacky Soap***, on the same day as Michelle Fowler on *EastEnders* gave birth to Vicky.

When this scene was first performed people enjoyed the story but didn't really laugh. However, I was certain it had unfulfilled potential. When over a year later, the idea of publishing the full version of *Too Much Punch For Judy* was first mooted, I suggested that I should develop a story version of *Happy Soap* to be included in the section for follow up work. It was agreed and I extended the narrative to create a short story... a process I thoroughly enjoyed!

I also wrote a couple of pages of back-up work specifically for the publication. I didn't have time to 'trial' this material, fortunately it worked really well and survives intact for this publication. It is now tried and tested forming a regular part of my school's Health Education/Drama curriculum. It is one of the few occasions where serious education can occur through the use of spontaneous and comic improvisation... students at our school really enjoy the quirky nature of this scheme of work!

Michelle Fowler (from *EastEnders*) moved to America and Vicky, for the time being, seems to have been forgotten (I have no doubt that she will return and by the time you read this may already have done so!), and it seemed that *Happy Soap* had been consigned to the Appendix of a book and would, if the truth be known, remain largely unused.

In the Summer of 1993 (when Brian Adam's song Everything I Do (*I Do it For You*) was wedged at the top of the British charts) I was in New Zealand promoting a tour of *Too Much Punch For Judy*. I had just completed an

NZBC interview about the play and was making my way back to my hotel room when the producer said he had read *Happy Soap* and wanted to make an animated film of it... what did I think? I was delighted and amazed... and could see that it would work really well.

I had visions of 'Disney'... however, my dream was brought to an abrupt halt. After a productive first meeting, I discovered the phone number I had been given was unobtainable... I later learned, the production company had gone bust! To this day I don't know how serious this man's interest was... but he did serve to place this quirky story of mine at the front of my consciousness again.

An animated film was beyond my control, but what I could do was to develop a play. On my return to England (with Brian Adams still at number 1!) I set to work adapting and developing this short 3-page story into a 20-page play with a view to having it published in its own right.

The first thing I did was to find a name for the location... I was really pleased with The Bower of Bliss! Remembering the *Python* animation I decided that the fairy tale characters (which in any case lacked any characterisation) needed to be unorthodox... a grumpy (rhyming) King, a smelly Queen for example, joined the already unconventional plotline, with the Princess effectively dying. Creating these stereotypical characters added comedy to the existing story. There were also some anomalies in the allegorical content of the story which had remained purely because of the rush to complete it in time... amazingly, in the earliest version the soap did not have the power to wash away limbs... so I 'tightened' it up for this new version and added various other absurdities.

There were times during the writing when I regretted the rhyme decision (why have I made life so difficult for myself?)... but it did serve to 'remove' the King from the Everyday Folk... and developed a life-long relationship between me and my Rhyming Dictionary... no-one should be without one!

Oaklands Youth Theatre in Southampton presented the play in 1992 and was shortlisted for the *Lloyds Theatre Challenge.* I won the Adjudicators Award for writing it at the local *Totton One Act Drama Festival*. I was heartened by this but, once again, it was put on the 'back burner'. I had this vague notion of developing it into a Musical and wrote four lyrics to melodies I had written years ago... but I did not have the ability to translate this into a written score. The opening song... music and lyrics survive for this publication... uses music originally belonging to a musical adaptation of Rumer Godden's *Kizzy* which I wrote way back in 1982!

The year before I had "stolen" The Bower of Bliss for the setting of ***The Most Absurd Xmas Musical in the World... Ever!*** James Holmes had composed the music to my absurd lyrics. The music was fantastic... and this had gone on to be published almost immediately! I suggested to James that he might like to put a few more of my bizarre lyrics to music. He agreed... although at that time I had said 'three or four songs'. I had no idea that I would do a complete overhaul of the script... (once finding myself writing to the familiar backdrop of England going out in the World Cup – again to Argentina – with the infamous Beckham sending off and Batty missed penalty) adding nine new songs. It wasn't until about the seventh song that James said "I thought there were only going to be four songs… how many more are there?"

There was one final, somewhat unexpected change that I chose to make... the title. My mum informed me that there was a product on sale called *Happy Liquid Soap*... so, to avoid any confusion (even though my ***Happy Soap*** had been around for the previous ten years), it became what it remains today… ***Wacky Soap***.

List of Characters

The Royal Family:
King Huff
Queen Huff
Princess Symbol

The Storyteller

Tom Common
Harriet Common
Dick Common (*Tom and Harriet's son)*
Clappum Common (*Tom and Harriet's daughter)*

Silly Guard
Page 1 & 2
Courtier
Artist in Residence

Everyday Goodies:
Pink; Kink; Shrink & Think (The Inks)
Old (Wo)Man
Squeak, Legless & Headless

Everyday Rebels:
Punk (also Elderly Stranger); Hunk; Junk & Skunk (the Unks)

Everyday Youth:
Quick, Kick & Slick (the Icks)

Chorus
Courtiers, the Everyday Folk, the Silly Guards,
the Youngies (*the Everyday Folk's children),* the Two Rebels

*The **Everyday Folk** are merrily dancing round a Maypole in a whimsical setting. **Harriet** and **Tom** stand at the side with their twin buggy, clapping and encouraging the dancers. When the play was first presented the castle was represented (and used) by a small inflatable bouncy castle. The Storyteller (who would be dressed quite bizarrely e.g. as a duck, a deep sea diver or as a Victorian in a swim suit), was situated in a small paddling pool with books in rather than water. The **Storyteller** opens his (could equally be her) large book, and begins to read.*

Storyteller: Once, in a far off whimsical land not so different from a bygone England, there lived a discontented King...

All: King Huff.

Storyteller: He ruled over The Bower of Bliss, and its... contented Everyday Folk. Just look at them, and listen to their rustic voices singing their wacky song!

SONG 1: WACKINESS IS ...

All:
Wackiness is... ears out here
(everyone pulls their ears as far as they will go),
deep in The Bower of Bliss
Wackiness is... the atmosphere, here in The Bower of Bliss

Tom & Harriet:
So why is our King humpy... grumpy all day long?

All:
Why won't he smile... why won't he smile?
Why won't he whistle a wacky tune?
Why is he so grim, we didn't vote for him
Let's hope he abdicates soon!

Wackiness is... the custard pie... thrown in The Bower of Bliss *(a custard pie is thrown in the face of one of the Everyday Folk)*
Wackiness is... politicised... here in The Bower of Bliss.

Tom & Harriet:
Why is our King humpy... grumpy all day long?

All:
Why won't he smile... why won't he smile?
Why won't he whistle a wacky tune?
Why is he so grim, we didn't vote for him
Let's hope he abdicates soon!

½ Group: **Wack atta wack atta –**
½ Group: **Wack atta wack atta –**
½ Group: **Wack atta –**

½ Group: **Wack atta –**
All: **Wackiness is...**

He's convinced we're discontented,
He won't accept that he's wrong.
This discontentment he's invented,
Let's call a denouement!
Tom/The Inks: **We're cheeky chappie's,**
We're happy all day long.
All: **Why won't he smile... why won't he smile?**
Why won't he whistle a wacky tune?
Why is he so grim, we didn't vote for him
Let's hope he abdicates soon.
½ Group : **Let's hope he abdicates...**
½ Group : **Let's hope he abdicates...**
All: **Let's hope he abdicates soon!**

Kink: Go on Tom Common... do your impersonation of our humpy grumpy...

All: Resplendent Rhyming Regent.

Shrink: Yeh!!! Go on.

Pink: Please!

All: Hooray!!! *(As Tom Common sets himself up to do his impersonation of King Huff.)*

Tom: *(Doing an impersonation of a very, very old man with white hair and a long beard.)*
What's all this merriment? You're not really happy!
Your dark mood reminds me of a... a filled
babies nappy! *(The Everyday Folk all laugh lots.)*

Harriet: *(Pushing her twin buggy with twin babies Dick & Clappum inside.)* Tom Common... I don't know why I married you... you're so embarrassing!

All: But very, very funny!

Think:	Anyway... on with the story! Storyteller?
Storyteller:	For three years, none of the Everyday Folk who lived in this whimsical land had seen their discontented King. No-one knew where he was...
Punk:	... and no-one really cared. *(The Everyday Folk all agree and laugh.)*
Storyteller:	Thank you Punk. Sadly for the King, not one of his subjects did care.
Hunk:	Why should we care?
Kink:	Frankly Hunk, I'm relieved that he's nowhere to be seen.
Junk:	I hope he never returns!
Skunk:	Then we'll never have to listen to his ridiculous speeches.
All:	Boring!
Punk:	And another thing!
All:	Yes Skunk.
Punk:	His stupid speeches always rhyme...
Hunk:	Just like some corny pantomime...
The Unks:	He always does it, every time.
All:	It should be a flipping crime... To speak like him... in rhyme! *(They all clap their hands and stamp their foot a la 'cheesy' pantomime!)*
Punk:	He's so miserable!
All:	*(General agreement.)* A miserable old wotsit!
Storyteller:	But, does King Huff deserve this reputation?
All:	Yes!!!
Storyteller:	Why?
Tom:	If we frown...
All:	He gets angry.

Harriet: And if we go so far as to cry he...

All: He goes completely berserk!

Storyteller: None of the Everyday Folk could understand why. (*Introducing them as he goes along)* Pink, Kink, Shrink, Punk, Hunk, Junk and Skunk, not to forget Tom and Harriet Common, and even their twin babies, Dick and Clappum Common... all of them just dismissed the Resplendent Rhyming Regent... as bad tempered...

All: Huffy! Just like his name!

Punk: On and on he goes, telling us to make sure that we have a 'happy ending'.

Hunk: That's all he ever thinks about, happy endings!

All: He thinks he lives in a fairy tale!

Storyteller: And yes, King Huff was determined to be a proper fairy tale King. His one and only desire was to secure a happy ending for all of the loyal Everyday Folk. In fact he had been so anxious about everything ending happily that he had made himself quite, quite miserable.

Pink: Well, where is he then?

Storyteller: That would be telling!

Think: ... Isn't that what you're there for... to...

All: ... Tell the story?

Storyteller: Yes, but you're <u>in</u> the story, so, before I continue I think you'd better go away.

All: We won't!

Storyteller: Oh yes you will!

All: Oh no we won't!

Storyteller: Oh yes you will!

All: Oh no we won't!

Storyteller: Suddenly without any warning at all, it started to pour down with rain and no-one had any umbrellas because it was the middle of summer.

Shrink: Oh no! It's suddenly started to rain!

Pink: And none of us have got any umbrellas!

Harriet: We're getting drenched!

Tom: The twins... the twins! *(Pulling the rainhood over the buggy.)*

All: I think we'd better go in.

Storyteller: So off they went to take shelter in their picturesque cottages.
King Huff meanwhile, had been so worried about everything ending happily, that he had decided he must do something.
For three years, he had locked himself away to work secretly in his palace laboratory to invent something to give his Everyday subjects more contentment than they could possibly have imagined. When finally he completed his experiments, he was so relieved that he...

King Huff: *(Entering clutching a small wash-bag.)*
Sang a song?

Storyteller: Alright then. (*The next line is said in a dead pan voice.)* When King Huff finally completed his experiments, he was so relieved that he sang a rather reflective song.

SONG 2: FIVE MINUTES OF FAME

King Huff:

Please let me claim five minutes of fame
So that everyone, everywhere, remembers my name
I'd like taps shaped like me put on everyone's bath
And have "Huff made us happy" for my epitaph
Such acclaim... from five minutes of fame.
Every day... Royals are criticised
People want to cut us down to size

Wacky Soap will show them all how much I care...
Final proof that I'm the Premiere with stacks of flair!

Please let me claim five minutes of fame
So that everyone, everywhere remembers my name
I'd like taps shaped like me put on everyone's bath
And have "Huff made us happy" for my epitaph
Such acclaim from five minutes of fame.
Five... minutes of fame.

Page! *(Enter Page)*
Summon before me the smelly Queen Huff.
My labours are over, I'll show her my stuff!
(Exit Page)

Voices: *(Off)* Summon the smelly Queen... Summon the smelly Queen... Summon the smelly Queen... Summon the smelly Queen.

Page 2: The King wishes to see you ma'am.

Queen: What King?

Page 2: King Huff Ma'am.

Queen: Can't it wait? There's something stuck down the toilet and the plunger's stuck and I'm in a right mess!

King: Page! Where is that odiferous Queen?
What's taking so long?

Page 1: Sirrah. She's unblocking the loo and it's making a pong!

King: Summon her now! I have something grand to tell.

Queen: *(Enters his chamber.)* Here I am darlin'. Sorry I smell!

King: The long sought happy ending, until now just a hope,
Is unequivocally ours... for I have invented this, and I'll call it Wacky Soap!
So, Queen Huff, speedily step in the shower...

And wonder at Wacky Soap's power...
When you lather your skin...
You will giggle and grin...
And hopefully stop smelling sour!

Storyteller: And although the courtiers tittered a little, the queen was not impressed!

Queen: Even if it does do all this... who'd care? I'm happy! Our subjects are happy no matter what you try to make us think. We don't need anything to make us happier! We're fine as we are!

King: Dearest, sweetest honey pie...
If you don't try it... I'm afraid I'll... I'll cry.

Storyteller: At which the whiffy Queen snatched the soap saying, rather coarsely...

Queen: Given that I am already happy, this soap has about as much chance of making me happier... as baked beans have curing my windy bottom!

Storyteller: So reluctantly, the pungent Queen tried the soap... just to please King Huff. A fanfare of trumpets played. The Courtiers averted their eyes as the sweat laden Queen undressed, and stepped in the royal shower to wash... first her hands and face, then her naughtiest bits and finally those awkward little crevices inside her ears that most of the Every-day Folk never bother to wash. Gradually, as the soap rubbed away the odours, a glowing sensation began to pass through her body...

Queen: This is flippin' amazin'!!!

Storyteller: ... And yes... she not only smelt pleasant but she was happier... wackier than she had ever been. She was radiating with joy, tickled pink, at one with the world and overflowing with giggles and feeling rather wacky. She leapt out of the shower and shouted:

Queen: Look! I can impersonate an elephant! *(she walks around the stage making elephant noises and waving her hand as though it was a trunk)*

Huffy, you've got to let Princess Symbol try this!

King: But first my heart's desire, don't I deserve a kiss?

Storyteller: A courtier carefully draped a towel around Queen Huff, before the royal snog!
Meanwhile their daughter, the beautiful Princess Symbol was summoned.

Princess Symbol: *(Running in and curtsying.)* Hello Daddy. Hello Mummy. Hello Storyteller. Hello audience. Why don't you smell Mummy? Why is everyone looking so happy? Is everything alright?

Queen: Your dad's done it! He's finally invented something to make sure we have a happy ending. He's invented a cool new soap... called Wacky Soap.
If ever you're feeling down, just find a bath, a shower, a stream or a bidet, and wash all your bad feelings away.

Symbol: I won't ever need that because I never have any bad feelings, I'm always happy!

Queen: *(Adopting American advertiser's voice.)* Believe me, once you've tried this Wacky Soap you'll never want to go back to your old soap!

Symbol: But I use Shamay.

King: If you don't try it, you'll never know...
Wacky Soap's cleansing afterglow.

Storyteller: King Huff didn't think he should force her to wash. So the only thing he could do was to cry *(King Huff cries)*... loudly, *(King Huff looks at the Storyteller, disgruntled, and cries very loudly)* in the hope that she'd feel sorry for him.

Queen: Please!

Storyteller: So, reluctantly, the gorgeous Princess Symbol tried the soap, just to please her mum and dad...
A fanfare of trumpets played. Most of the Courtiers averted their eyes as the nubile Princess Symbol undressed and stepped in the royal shower to wash.

Gradually, as the soap rubbed into her skin, a glowing sensation began to pass through her body...

Symbol: This is amazing!

Queen: Now will you swap your bar of Wacky Soap for two bars of old Shamay?

Symbol: No fear. I'll always use Wacky Soap from now on!

Storyteller: The Royal Huffs were delighted. Not only did this new invention clean people...

Queen: It stopped them stinking!

Storyteller: ... and also made them happy... and prone to do the wackiest of things.

Queen & Symbol: Look! We can both impersonate elephants! *(they walk around making elephant noises and waving their hands as though they were trunks)*

Royal Family: Hurrah!

Storyteller: And, even though he had not been using the Wacky Soap, King Huff felt happier than he had ever been before in his entire life. King Huff was happy because he'd found a way to make other people happy. He wanted everyone in his Kingdom to use his Wacky Soap... and then everyone, including King Huff, could choose to be happy... wacky, whenever they wanted.

King: In recognition Page arrange a Festive
Celebration Scrub
Deck the streets with portable showers and
tables full of grub.
Inform the Everyday Folk that I to all of
them will speak
In the Market square at 1pm. this day next week.
That night will be a festival, but don't
explain the reason
Just tell them to come with a rubber duck or else be
tried for treason!

Storyteller: And with that King Huff returned to his laboratory to produce sufficient Wacky Soap for his off the wall idea... A Festive Celebration Scrub.
The Everyday Folk watched in amazement as plumbers worked up and down the picturesque streets installing modern portable shower units, baths, basins and bidets.

All: What a very strange sight!

Storyteller: They chorused with a puzzled look on their country bumpkin faces. The next morning they were horrified...

All: Aaaaargh!

Storyteller: ... horrified to discover gaudy posters dotted along the picturesque streets, telling them that the Resplendent Rhyming Regent wanted to address them all, in six days time.

Think: Custard Pies...

Kink: ... and ears out here *(they all pull ears)*

Think & Kink: ... is one thing, but this...

All: This is taking wackiness too far!

Tom: What can he be planning?

Storyteller: So curious they were... that without much of a warning they all burst into an absurdly appropriate song.

SONG 3: **THE GOOD OLD DAYS**

Tom: **Weird goings on... making no sense**
What can explain these crazy events?

Harriet: **Stupid ideas... baths in the street**
Odd and absurd and not very discrete!

Punk: **We can't understand what is planned.**
Such extreme ideas must be banned!

<u>*Refrain*</u>

All: **The good old days! The good old days!**
It was never so strange in the good old days
The good old days! The good old days!
We'll never quite get used to all these newer ways.

Old (Wo)Man: **It was never like this... in The Bower of Bliss**
When I was knee-high to a baby shuttlecock!

All: **The good old days! The good old days**
Why can't we turn back the clock?
Repeat Refrain
with an extended ending:
Tick-tock, tick-tock, tick-tock, tick...
Tick-tock, tick-tock, tick-tock, tick...
Why can't we turn back the clock?

Storyteller: By one minute to one on the appointed day a large crowd gathered around the market square, each one clutching their rubber duck...

All: ... And feeling really silly!

Storyteller: No-one could work out what had made King Huff decide to show himself after these three years.

1/2 E. Folk: I wonder why King Huff wants to see us today.

Other 1/2: We can't work it out! Can you?

First 1/2: No! We can't work it out either!

Storyteller: *(Pronouncing -- through a microphone? – menacingly with a controller-like quality.)*
Beware: He who talks of happiness... summons grief.

All: *(Looking above and around them in sheer panic. Screaming in fear.)* Aaaaargh!!!!

1/2 E. Folk: Who was that?

Other 1/2: Don't know!

All: Think... tell us what it means.

Think: It was some kind of warning... but... but I don't understand it.

Pink:	If Think doesn't understand...
Shrink:	... no-one will!
All:	Aaaaaargh!!!
Hunk:	Maybe we were imagining it?
The Unks:	Yeh. Let's say we were!
All:	*(Obediently)* We were imagining it.
Tom:	That's a relief!
All:	Phew!!! Can we get on with the story?
Storyteller:	Finally the big clock in the market-place struck one. *(It does so.)*
All:	*(To Storyteller.)* Well? Where is King Huff then?
Storyteller:	He's behind you!
Skunk:	He must be on his own then.
All:	Why's that?
Skunk:	I can't smell his Mrs.
Storyteller:	She's here as well!
All:	She can't be!
Storyteller:	She is!
All:	*(They look the wrong way.)* Where?
Storyteller:	There!
All:	Where?
Storyteller:	There!
All:	Oh no they're not.
Storyteller:	*(Encouraging the audience to participate.)* Oh yes they are!
All:	Oh no they're not.
Storyteller:	*(Encouraging the audience to participate.)* Oh yes they are!
All:	Oh no they're not.

Storyteller: *(Encouraging the audience to participate.)*
Oh yes they are!

All: Oh no they're not.

Storyteller: *(Encouraging the audience to participate.)*
Oh yes they are!

All: Oh no they're not.

Storyteller: *(Encouraging the audience to participate.)*
Oh yes they are!

All: *(Seeing him.)* Oh yes they are!

King: You seem surprised to see your King.

All: It's been three long years without hearing a thing!

Skunk: And we couldn't smell your Mrs. *(Everyone tries to shut Skunk up!)*

King: Me, my sweet smelling wife and my glamorous daughter .. have so much to tell.
But first I must ask... how are you? Are you well?

Tom: Things are much the same for us Sirrah.

Storyteller: King Huff took this to mean that his subjects were unhappy.

King: All of you will be delighted to hear... That sadness you need no more fear.

Storyteller: His subjects looked surprised... *(They do so)*... and then worried... *(They do so.)*

King: A secure and happy ending, until now just a hope... Is unequivocally ours, for I have invented this... and I call it... *(He holds a bar of Wacky Soap aloft.)*
Wacky Soap!

All: We don't want a happy ending.

Storyteller: Oh yes you do!

Tom: Shut-up Storyteller!
Sorry King. *(To the Storyteller.)* You've made me forget what I was going to...

Think: What is this Wacky Soap? What does it do?

King: It will, I promise, work wonders for you!
It cleans away both dirt and discontent.

Queen: ... And leaves you clean and radiant *(sic)*!

Skunk: Is this what stopped your Mrs from smelling?

Storyteller: The Everyday Folk of The Bower of Bliss looked at one another silently. No-one dared to say anything. *(A moment of uncomfortable silence.)*

Queen: Yes. And I shall never smell, burp or pass wind again! Give King Huff a clap... give him a cheer! *(They all clap and cheer enthusiastically... but no-one else joins in.)* So... are you going to try the soap?

Skunk: If it stopped her from smelling and put a smile on her face it must be worth a go.

Tom: But apart from you Skunk, we don't smell.

Junk: And we're all really happy!

All: Look! *(They all pull happy faces and dance and do other things associated with 'wackiness'.)*

The Inks: We all live in picturesque cottages.

All: Three or four bedrooms... each.

Pink: We all have beautiful children.

Punk: Well mannered.

All: Perfectly behaved!

Harriet: We all have lovely cars.

Junk: Digital TVs!

Tom: *(Picking a phone out of the buggy)*...
Mobile phones!

Kink: And bright yellow bananas.

All: What?

Kink: Sometimes they're a bit brown... but not very often!

All: King Huff... we speak as one! We're happy enough. We do not need your soap!

King: Oh yes you do!

All: Oh no we don't!

King: Oh yes you do!

All: Oh no we don't!

Tom: We use Shamay.

Harriet: That's why we all look so young and beautiful.

All: We don't need your soap! Listen!
(They start to sing Wackiness Is...)

Queen: Shut up!!!
Shut up!!! *(Silence)*

Storyteller: The silence that fell on the market square was broken only moments later by the delicate footsteps of the adorable Princess Symbol walking towards the crowd. She stood confidently in front of the royal microphone. The crowd gasped as they heard for the first time the sweetness of her royal voice.

SONG 4: **TRANSPORTED**

*(Falteringly at first...
gradually growing in confidence.)*

Princess Symbol:

**I, like you, used Shamay.
Now, I've learnt the Wacky Soap way.
Never before have I been so tickled pink
As now when I'm washing at my royal sink.**

**I've been transported...
I'm floating on cloud nine
I'm aquanaughted... and feeling quite divine
Now I realise my life was not complete
Never has a good old wash been such a
flipping treat!
Life is complete... Share in this treat...**

The Royal Family and Courtiers:

You'll be transported...
You'll float upon cloud nine
Be aquanaughted... and feel quite divine
Try to realise your life is not complete
Never has your Shamay bar been
quite so obsolete.
Share in this treat... Share in this treat.

(The music continues under the following lines of dialogue.)

Courtier: *(Clutching two bars of Shamay.)* Would you swap these two bars of ordinary Shamay for one of your Wacky Soap bars?

Symbol: Certainly not! I'll always use Wacky Soap from now on. *(The Everyday Folk vomit in unison... mimed!)*

Think: Some of us may be simple but we're not going to be taken in by that twaddle!

Queen & Symbol: But none of you can do elephant impressions! *(They demonstrate.)*

All: OK then, we'll give it a go!

All:

We'll be transported...
We'll float upon cloud nine
Be aquanaughted... and feel quite divine
We will realise our life is not complete
Never has our Shamay bar been
quite so obsolete.
As we share... share this treat.

(The Everyday Folk cheer the Royal Family.)

Queen: Come on then, what are you waiting for? Off with your clothes!

Storyteller: The courtiers smirked and averted their eyes as the...

All: No way! We're not stripping off!

Storyteller: The courtiers smirked and averted their eyes... but... no-one took their clothes off.

Queen: You can't use the soap with your clothes on!

Tom: We're not stripping off in broad daylight.

Hunk: Not for you anyway!

All: Not for anyone.

King: I quite agree but tonight when it's dark
Taking your clothes off will seem quite a lark
For I have arranged a special event...
A Celebration Scrub with a Wacky Soap scent.
Wash and be merry and dance in the street...
Sing in the aisles or just put soap on your feet.
Page, hand a free sample to all who are here...
With money off vouchers for the rest of the year.

Storyteller: Somewhat bemused, the Everyday Folk wandered back to their picturesque cottages to collect their towels and flannels. What an adventure lay before them they thought.

All: No we didn't! *(They exit.)*

Storyteller: They didn't know the half of it! Meanwhile, the Royal Huffs returned to Bliss Palace.

Symbol: Daddy can I have a crate of Wacky Soap?

King: *(Imploring a courtier to pass her two large crates of Wacky Soap.)* Take two crates, Princess Symbol, my dear
It's clear that you think Wacky Soap's the hit of the year.

Symbol: Yes I do Daddy... Yes I do!

Storyteller: And with that he kissed her goodnight, and, weary from his years of invention he retired, with his fragrant Queen, to his oh so comfortable Royal Water Bed. He closed his eyes and drifted into the world of Happy Ever After Endings he felt sure that he could now inhabit. He slept peacefully throughout the night.
Meanwhile the curvaceous Princess Symbol undressed...

Symbol: *(To an onlooking Courtier.)* Oi!!! *(She makes sure she cannot be seen.)*

Storyteller: ... and stepped into her royal shower, planning to stay there all night long, washing and washing, to make herself more and more happy. Bliss Palace fell silent, except for the sound of the Princess Symbol singing *I'm Transported* from time to time in the shower. The Bower of Bliss was altogether a different picture, rocking and rolling...

All: *(Entering as elephants)*... and doing some impressive elephant impressions!

SONG 5: CELEBRATION SCRUB

(Clearly the addition of a bubble machine will aid the presentation of this song!)

Group 1: **We're in love with these Wacky Soap bars**
So rip off your clothes and wash beneath the stars

Group 2: **Work up a lather and wallow in the suds**
Spilling loads of water in celebrat'ry floods!

Refrain

All: **A rub-a-dubba dub in a celebration scrub**
With a rubber-dubba duck for the King
We'll hey-diddle-diddle with a grin and a giggle
As we rub-a-dub our diddles and sing!
Celebration... celebration... celebration scrub
Celebration... celebration... washing in a tub
Celebration... Rub - a dub - dub - dub!

Tom: **What a shock that King Huff made this stuff**
Harriet: **Our only concern is that there is not enough.**
Think: **The Bower of Bliss has never been like this**
Skunk: **Gaining such a thrill from obsessive cleanliness**

Refrain:

All: **A rub-a-dubba dub... etc.**

Rap:

Punk: **Old King Huff ain't really so rough**
He's a ruler with his heart in the right place
He's a merry ol' soul with his Wacky Soap stuff

And merry ol' souls are we...
Merry ol' souls are we!

Refrain:

All: **A rub-a-dubba dub... etc.**

Storyteller: The Bower of Bliss was more than content.

Tom: What a celebration!

Storyteller: The Wacky Soap, that everyone doubted...

Tom & Harriet: ... and no-one really wanted...

Storyteller: ... did make everyone cleaner... and happier.

Think: Even Skunk smelt fresh!!!

All: Public bathing!

Skunk: Why haven't we done it before?

All: Splashing... splooshing!

Shrink: Bubbles everywhere.

Kink: "Quack quack", said the rubber duck.

Storyteller: How fortunate that there was no water shortage in The Bower of Bliss because the baths, showers, basins and bidets were being used almost non-stop from the moment the Celebration Scrub began.

All: Wash and be merry.

Punk: Who'd 've ever thought that we'd be standing here as naked as the day we were born saying...

All: Good old King Huff!

Hunk: Not me.

Junk: Nor me!

All: Nor me!

Tom: Good old King Huff!

All: Long may he reign!

Hunk: And much Wacky Soap may he produce!

Skunk:	I'll wash to that!
All:	Good old King Huff! *(Each word in this motif is accompanied by a chorally mimed action!)* Flannel! Soap! Wash! Giggle! Jump for joy! *(As they jump they make out that they have revealed their 'naughty bits!'... this scene is of course done fully clothed but the acting/reacting should make out that they are all naked.)* Whoops! *(They attempt to cover themselves up with a towel... mimed)* Towel.
Storyteller:	But, as time wore on, strange things began to happen...
All:	Oh no! Strange things are beginning to happen!
Storyteller:	Things that even King Huff could not have predicted! This Wacky Soap clearly had powers that King Huff was not aware of. It seemed that those who used a little of the soap giggled and smiled and really quite enjoyed themselves doing the most amazing elephant impressions. *(They all lumber around as elephants trumpeting loudly.)*
Storyteller:	But those who continued washing with this tempting soap, long after most had returned to their quilted beds, discovered that the soap began to wash away their common-sense.
Pink & Think:	Look at us... we can be flying elephants... just like Dumbo. *(They jump, flapping their arms wildly, and fall to the ground in a heap.)*
Hunk & Junk:	Look at us! We can hit people with our trunks! *(A brief fight ensues.)* Sometimes we hit them so hard... they die! *(Some are killed.)*
Shrink:	Look at me! I can throw this boulder... *(Mimes the throwing of the boulder – cartoon style – and the noise it makes as it crash lands)*... and I don't care where it lands! *(Others join in the fun.)*

All:	Riot!
Storyteller:	And feeling as though they had the strength of an elephant, they, and many like them, wrought destruction upon The Bower of Bliss.
The Unks:	And we don't care one bit!
All:	We're only pretending to be elephants! *(They trumpet very loudly. Then a moment of silence.)*
Storyteller:	Worse still, were those, hidden away in corners, not daring to come out, who had used even more soap, and had washed parts of their bodies clean away.
Harriet:	*(Referring to her own... now no longer there.)* Hands... arms...
Legless:	*(Referring to his/her own... now no longer there.)* Legs... *(finally referring to Headless who walks on stage with no visible head.)* Heads.
Squeak:	*(Referring to his/her own... now no longer there... if male, to be said in a falsetto voice)* Naughty bits!
Storyteller:	... nothing was safe from the dazzling power of King Huffs 'great' invention... Wacky Soap. Finally, everyone who was able, returned to their picturesque cottages.
Tom:	Harriet!
Harriet:	Tom!
Tom:	I've been looking everywhere for you?
Harriet:	You'll never believe what's happened!
Tom:	What has happened?
Harriet:	Wacky Soap has washed my arms away!
Tom:	Lucky I was holding the baby!
Harriet:	You always manage to say the right thing... I do love you.
Tom:	And I love you.
Harriet:	Let's go back to our picturesque cottage.
Tom::	We can't!

Harriet:	Yes we can!
Tom:	We can't. Look! *(They turn to look in melodramatic slow motion unison.)*
Harriet:	Oh No!!!
Tom:	Oh Yes!!!
Harriet:	Let's tell the Storyteller... I'm sure he'll do something about it!
Tom & Harriet:	*(Complaining to the Storyteller.)* Our picturesque cottage has been daubed with graffiti!
Pink:	*(Complaining to the Storyteller.)* My picturesque cottage has been broken into… all my things have gone!
Kink:	*(Complaining to the Storyteller.)* Mine's been ransacked!
Shrink:	*(Complaining to the Storyteller.)* Mine's been burnt to the ground!
All (except the ...Unks):	*(To the Storyteller.)* Why have you allowed this to happen?
The Unks:	*(Skipping on.)* Our picturesque cottages are fine! We've got Rottweilers!!! *(They Exit.)*
All (except the ...Unks):	We need to speak to King Huff.
Storyteller:	The Everyday Folk were furious, and, even though it was the middle of the night, angrily marched towards Bliss Palace *(They march in what the Storyteller believes to be the 'wrong' direction)...* no... <u>towards</u> Bliss Palace... *(They turn and march in the opposite direction)...* to confront their now contented, but sleeping King.
Think:	This way... I know a shortcut! *(They turn back the way they were originally facing, and in the introduction to the following song find unusual objects to arm themselves with and re-arrange themselves as an army.)*

Storyteller: And as they marched... they sang to bolster their spirits... and make this section of the play slightly more enjoyable!

SONG 6: **RIOT... RIOT!**

All (except the ... Unks):
Riot... Riot... devastation, desecration
Abdication must be on the cards.
Riot... Riot... violation of our nation
We want Huff without his bodyguards!
We're determined that King Huff will pay
For everything that happened yesterday

Tom:
This stupid, rhyming King must have his features re-arranged

Legless:
The stupid law won't help us so we'll help ourselves

All:
We'll take up arms and fight this stupid rhy...ming King

The Bower of Bliss has never seen such anger

Tom & Harriet:
The Bower of Bliss has never been so down

2 Everydays:
Wacky Soap has surely ended King Huff's right to the crown

All:
The Bower of Bliss has never seen such sadness

Tom & Harriet:
As when we saw this soap wash limbs away

2 Everydays:
Wacky Soap will be remembered as King Huff's final day!

All:
Riot... Riot... devastation, desecration
Abdication must be on the cards.
Riot... Riot... violation of our nation
We want Huff without his bodyguards!
We're determined that King Huff will pay
For everything that happened yesterday

1/2 Group:
This stupid, rhyming King must have his features re-arranged
The stupid law won't help us so we'll help ourselves

Other 1/2 Group:
We'll take up arms and fight this stupid rhy...ming King

All:
Riot... Riot... Riot... Riot... Riot... Riot... Riot!!!

Storyteller: The silly guards, failing to understand what was happening, and not wanting the royal family to be disturbed, forcefully tried to stop the Everyday subjects from passing.

Silly Guards: Halt... who goes there!

All: Out of our way...

Silly Guards: Stop!!!

All: Else what?

Silly Guards: Else... *(All the Silly Guards pull faces and make noises at the Everyday Folk.)*

All: We won't tell you again.

Silly Guards. Please don't be too rough with us!

Storyteller: The Everyday Folk turned on the silly, Silly Guards. Battles erupted up and down the picturesque streets. *(Cameo scenes can be set up for the Storyteller to walk through as though a guide to this battle.)* Objects were thrown *(an example of this happens),* ridiculous weapons were fired *(an example of this happens),* and much was damaged in The Bower of Bliss. Picturesque buildings were destroyed, one after the other, as the Silly Guards made a futile attempt to quell this risible riot.

Silly Guards: Please stop it. Pleeeease! Pretty please with shiny brass knobs and icing on top!

Storyteller: Chaos and destruction ruled the night that had begun as the Festive Celebration Scrub.
Early the next morning King Huff awoke, expecting to be the hero of the day, and excitedly asked one of his courtiers to draw back his royal curtains.
He stood on his royal balcony proudly, to survey what he thought would be a much happier Bower of Bliss, but, there in his courtyard were gathered what looked like an army of his Everyday Subjects... weeping, wailing, shouting and brandishing various everyday objects not normally thought of as weapons.

Various Everyday Folk:	{We thought we could trust you!} {Look what you have done!}
Tom & Harriet:	Our picturesque cottage has been daubed with graffiti
Pink:	Mine's been broken into... all my things have gone
Kink:	Mine's been ransacked
Shrink:	Mine's been burnt to the ground!
King Huff:	It cannot be my Wacky Soap... it's done me no harm. Au contraire... when I feel stressed it makes me feel calm!
Harriet:	Wacky Soap washed away my arms!
Legless:	And my legs... her head *(Points to Headless)*.
Squeak:	And my naughty bits have completely disappeared!
Storyteller:	King Huff was speechless... well, nearly speechless.
King:	I must admit I don't know what to say... Are you sure you can blame my Wacky Soap for causing this affray?
Punk:	Well me and my Everyday mates had a great time! We'd like to buy some more.
King:	I'll sell you as much as you like... I've made half a tonne Come on speak up I'm sure some others had fun.
Hunk:	Well King Huff. I liked it 'cos it's good for my everyday business... I'm a shower installer.
Punk:	*(To the Everyday Folk)* So long as you're sensible with it, it can do you no harm!
Hunk:	Skunk, tell him what you think.
Skunk:	Noble King Huff, your invention is wonderful. Wacky Soap has stopped me from smelling and made me happy. It's the greatest thing since...
The Unks:	Sliced bread.

Junk: We don't have sliced bread!

All (others): Shut-up!

Tom: Wacky Soap is dangerous.

All: It should be banned!

King: Wacky Soap is here to stay
To wash your troubles clean away!
These people here *(referring to the Unks)* are the proof I need
Wacky Soap remains as my good deed.

Think: King Huff this is no joke! You must stop this soap before it does more damage.

Tom & Harriet: We want you to do something now!

All (except the ...Unks): Or else there'll be trouble.

The Unks: Over our dead bodies. *(The Unks go to attack the others but stop as they hear the Queen's entrance.)*

Queen: *(Entering in a panic.)* Fl i i i i pping heck!
Huff... Huff, come quick I have something to tell!

King: Not now my dear, I have a riot to quell!

Queen: Huffy darling, Huffy dear...
If you do not adhere...
To what I say, severe...
... will be your punishment. I'll thrust a spear...
up your rear...
And send you screaming through the stratosphere!
So, if you don't want a scabby bottomed souvenir...
Get your bottom over here...
And make it quick!

King: *(Loudly to the throng.)*
Suddenly, I'm feeling rather green...
I must inside to see my Queen!

All (except the ...Unks): If you can't sort this out King Huff, we'll have you on the guillotine!

Storyteller: And with that threat ringing in his ears King Huff went inside.

All (except the ...Unks): How dare he walk away from us.

SONG 7: RIOT ... RIOT! *(REPRISE)*

All:

Riot... Riot... devastation, desecration
Abdication must be on the cards.
Riot... Riot... violation of our nation
We want Huff without his bodyguards!
We're determined that King Huff will pay
For everything that happened yesterday
This stupid, rhyming King must have his features re-arranged
The stupid law won't help us so we'll help ourselves
We'll take up arms and fight this stupid rhy...ming King

Riot... Riot... Riot... Riot... Riot... Riot... Riot!!!

(They exit.)

Queen: *(Now inside Bliss Palace.)*
I know not how to tell you this news.

King: I hope that it will me amuse.

Queen: I fear it won't King Huff... it's worse than bad...
This news will make you very sad!

King: Spit it out! Tell me do!...
So I can stop this hullabaloo!

Queen: Last night Symbol washed in her royal shower...
She used your Wacky Soap hour after hour...
This morning when I went to her room to see 'er...
I found that she had completely disappeared!...
Poor girl, she must have washed herself away...
For there upon her bed, was an empty crate of Wacky Soap, and, her favourite negligé.

King: Oh Queen, oh Queen!

Storyteller: Sobbed poor King Huff.

King: I can't go on, life's far too tough.

Storyteller: And the King sat down and wondered what he should do.

King: I know! I'll sing a song for you.

Queen: Oh what a wonderful idea... that'll make me feel much better!

Storyteller: And so he did... albeit a shortened reprise of one you've already heard.

SONG 8: FIVE MINUTES OF FAME *(REPRISE)*

King Huff:
I didn't dream five minutes of fame
Could make everyone, everywhere discredit my name
How can so much distress come from having a bath
Now I dare not visu'lise my epitaph?

King & Queen:
Such shame from five minutes of fame.
Five minutes of fame.

Storyteller: His subjects were discontented. His Queen was discontented, and his daughter, the Princess Symbol, had, it seemed, dematerialised! The newly contented King, of this once contented Kingdom, returned to his discontented state of mind. Bravely King Huff and his Queen returned to the balcony to make an announcement.

King: I did what I did for the good of our land...

King & Queen: How it's gone so wrong we just don't understand.

King: I had no idea when one lathered too long...
There was any risk that things could go so wrong.
What has happened to you, I truly regret...

King & Queen: Wacky Soap is a most deadly threat...

King: We too have been affected, last night the Princess Symbol washed herself away...
So, I hereby announce a ban of Wacky Soap

without delay...
In taking this action I have no hesitation...

Queen: *(Aside.)* Before it washes out all of our nation.

Storyteller: And with that King Huff immediately stopped production.

Punk: Don't be so daft!

Storyteller: Called out a figure stepping out from the public shower placed closest to Bliss Palace.

Punk: Me and my Everyday friends had a great time!

Storyteller: A small group of Everyday Folk were standing nearby, all wearing towels, giggling and talking contentedly to their rubber ducks.

Punk: You might be able to stop production within the palace walls, but, you can't stop me and my mates from making it.

All (except the Unks): Oh yes we can!

The Unks: Oh no you can't!

All (except the Unks): Oh yes we can!

The Unks: Oh no you can't!

All (except the Unks): Oh yes we can! Anyway... you don't know how to! Hah!

Junk: I haven't mentioned this before but, I'm an investigative Scientist and I know how it's made. *(Gasps from the Everyday Folk.)* So you can't stop me from analysing the soap and manufacturing it, if necessary, outside your precious kingdom.

Punk: And if ever there's a demand for it to be sold here in The Bower of Bliss... we'll, find a way... we'll be back!

The Unks: So ner! *(They make as if to exit.)*

Punk: Oh by the way, thanks King Huff, you wanted to make your subjects happy... well, you've made us very happy.

Skunk: Very, very happy.

Punk: And now you'll make us rich. I'd hate you to think that we were being greedy, so what do you say to a ten per cent cut in the Wacky Soap profits?

Storyteller: Now come on Punk! I didn't put those words in your mouth! How can he possibly agree with that?

Punk: That's your problem Storyteller... but remember... if he doesn't... the story would have to end here, and... well... it isn't really a very good ending... is it?

Storyteller: *(Resigned)* OK then... ask him again then!

Punk: So, King Huff, what do you say to a ten per cent cut in the Wacky Soap profits?

Storyteller: King Huff's response was quick... and not at all what either I or the Everyday Folk were expecting.

King: I'll take the ten per cent on offer...
And put it in the royal coffer.

The Unks: Good on ya King Huff. We'll be in touch!
(They exit.)

Storyteller: And with that, Punk, Hunk, Junk and Skunk, left, wearing only their towels, clutching their rubber ducks, and as many bars of Wacky Soap as their greedy arms could carry.
(The Unks exit.)
The Everyday Folk of The Bower of Bliss
were incensed!

All: We're incensed!

Pink: Bring on the guillotine...

All: Off with his head!

Storyteller: The Queen, who had already lost one of her family that morning was petrified...

Queen: Listen... Huffy will know what to do... Huffy will come up with a solution... just give him a chance!

All: Off with his head!

Queen: Just listen to what he has to say!

All: Off with his head!

Storyteller: But did King Huff have anything to say?
(He moves forward.) He stood before the crowd, his hands shaking and royal sweat fermenting on his royal brow. The crowd fell silent.

King: Without these profits we'll not be able to pay...
To sort out the devastation that has hit us today.
So, we'll open a fund in our dear daughter's name...
To fund the repairs and then to proclaim...
The truth of Wacky Soap, and what harm it can do...
To people such as me or you.

Storyteller: And with that, the people cheered...

All: Hooray!

Storyteller: ... and said that King Huff's reply proved that he was, after all, a wise old resplendent rhyming King.

All: What a wise old Resplendent Rhyming Regent he is!

Storyteller: There was also some good news for the Everyday Folk. After a few days those who had washed bits of themselves away found that they returned.

Tom: Harriet!

Harriet: Tom?

Tom: Look... your arms are back!

Harriet: And I didn't even notice! I can't believe it!

Storyteller: Everyone was so excited.

All: Yippee! Look all our bits have returned!

Squeak: And Mrs Squeak is having a baby!!!

(Everyone cheers)

Storyteller: There was much relief...

All: Phew!!!

Storyteller: But, alas, not for those who had washed themselves clean away. It soon became clear that they had gone for ever... and there was much grieving in The Bower of Bliss.

All: *(Singing a la plainsong.)* We are so sad at the loss of our friends. A-men.

Storyteller: Although the Royal Huffs always smiled when seen by the Everyday Folk, they were broken hearted by the loss of their daughter, the Princess Symbol. Many royal tears were wept and, without her, Bliss Palace seemed strangely empty. No-one could bring Princess Symbol back. She, like many others, was gone for ever.
Strangely King Huff found contentment.
He gradually came to understand that true contentment could never...

All: Never!!!

Storyteller: Never be manufactured. He recalled the day when his wife, the Queen, first tried the soap when he felt happier than he had ever felt before and he had not even used it... King Huff had learnt something... something very significant.

King Huff: Lasting happiness comes from within
Not from a quick fix lather on your skin ..
Happiness is deeper than an elephant impression.

Storyteller: And for once... the Resplendent Rhyming Regent was stuck for a rhyme. No matter... because for the first time King Huff been... well... he'd been profound!
For the next year the Everyday Folk of The Bower of Bliss thought about those words and attempted to live by them.

All: Happiness is deeper than an elephant impression.

Storyteller: That sure sounded like a corny cue for a song! *(The introduction strikes up.)* The interval's next so you'll have a few moments to relieve yourselves... and then back for the unmissable...

All: Second half!

SONG 9: HAPPINESS IS...
(REPRISE OF WACKINESS IS...)

All: **Happiness is... living here, deep in The Bower of Bliss**

Tom: **Happiness is... the atmosphere, here in The Bower of Bliss**

All: **We're cheeky chappies we're joking all day long**
We'll make you laugh... We'll make you smile
We'll make you whistle this happy tune.
Shake you by the hand... and pat you on the back...
Why don't you visit The Bower of Bliss... soon...
Why don't you visit... Why don't you visit
Why don't you visit us soon!

Storyteller: The People of The Bower of Bliss lived contentedly in their makeshift houses, while the damaged picturesque cottages were being replaced by brand spanking new blocks, a fantastic "new" idea of the really clever architects...

All: Oi! Storyteller!

Storyteller: What?

All: What are you doing?

Storyteller: What do you mean?

Tom: Shouldn't you always start the Second part of the show off with a song... you know, to get everyone back into the swing of things.

Harriet: And to cover the noise of anyone in the audience coming in late.

All: ... arriving late! *(Accusing looks if appropriate.)*

Storyteller: Go on then... if you know one about The Bower of Bliss New Town?

All: *(Putting on fake American accents.)* Just so happens that we do!

SONG 10: **THE NEW TOWN DREAM**

(The song is sung as the scenery is changed/revealed to become ultra modern.)

All: *(in fake American accents)*

Wonder at our New Town...
Bower of Bliss New Town
A dream-land to bring up our children
Jealous of our New town?
Bower of Bliss New Town
Designer dreams... see how they build 'em

Mapping to perfection...
Nothing needs correction
The New Town dream has come true!
Look! Wacky in our backyard...
Architects have worked so hard
Wow! Modernity so vast is...

Blotting out the Old Town past
The New Town dream has come true
The New Town dream has come true.

Storyteller: *(exaggeratedly British accent)*
The quaint old skyline is vanishing fast
Blotting out memories of the past
Sparkley debacle... shimmers and shines
Boring designs... everything in lines
Still the Everyday Folk proclaim
Still the Everyday Folk proclaim

All: **Wonder at our New town etc.**

Storyteller: The Bower of Bliss New Town was paid for by the Wacky Soap profits that poured in from lands so far away that even King Huff had never heard of them. Everything seemed to be going so well.

All: It is!

Tom: Don't go and mess it up.

Storyteller: Would I dare to threaten The Bower of Bliss and its fairy tale ending by the return of King Huff's own invention... the Wacky Soap?

All: Yes!

Storyteller: One generation later, in the form of Punk, in disguise as a very strange old man, carrying a mysterious old sack... that threat arrived at the borders of The Bower of Bliss.

Punk: *(Punk in a transparent/obvious, but elaborate "Elderly Stranger" disguise. (S)He feigns a 'mysterious' voice.)* Good morrow sir. Be this The Bower of Bliss?

Silly Guard: Yes, and I am a Silly Guard! Who are you?

Punk: I be an Elderly Stranger. I have travelled many moons.

Silly Guard: Exactly how strange are you?

Punk: I do take on the form of an elephant! *(Does an extravagant elephant impression.)*

Silly Guard: Wow that's brilliant!

Punk:	And elephants do, sometimes, take silly guards for eating.
Silly Guard:	Not a particularly sensible thing to say... given that I am a Silly Guard, and I've got a ridiculous water pistol!
Punk:	I did tell thee I be strange!
Silly Guard:	Be that as it may, I hardly think I'm going to allow you into The Bower of Bliss now am I? Everyone in The Bower of Bliss has to be happy and do things that lead to a more fulfilled life and ultimately... a happy ending.
Punk:	My conjurings will make people curve their lips in an upward direction.
Silly Guard:	Yes! I suppose so! Let me unlock these giant gates and then you'd better go on in! *(Suddenly turning.)* Er, just before you go in... what's that on your back?
Punk:	This be *(a most meaningful pause!)*... a mysterious sack.
Silly Guard:	It doesn't look particularly mysterious to me!
Punk:	Pray... take a peek inside.
Silly Guard:	Soap? Soap? More soap?
Punk:	Aye, 'tis so. I be here to offer all ye Everyday Folk a worthwhile exchange. I bid thy people give me their unwanted soap and I will grant each of them a new bar of Freebie Soap.
Silly Guard:	You'll exchange old, used bars of soap for this new Freebie Soap. That seems to be a very good deal! What's the catch?
Punk:	There be none... dost thou not recall... this is a fable.
Silly Guard:	Aren't... aren't there 'baddies', in fables?
Punk:	Thou silly, Silly Guard! Is my form that of a Bad'un? If I were a baddie... they'd *(referring to the audience)* make the boo and hiss sounds. *(Storyteller holds up*

	boo and hiss signs. If the audience do respond by booing/hissing, the salesperson should pass it of by saying:) Ignore their folly and behold my idea. I bid you, let me enter The Bower of Bliss and I will hand thee two bars of this Freebie Soap. *(Offers two bars from the sack.)*
Silly Guard:	*(Eagerly taking the soap.)* Can't really lose, can I?
Punk:	Fare ye well young guard, and be ye sure not to overwash with this lest ye disappear.
Storyteller:	But before the stranger could finish his/her sentence the Silly Guard had disappeared into his functional rest room to wash his somewhat grimy hands. He came back out on duty, giggling away to himself and occasionally trumpeting like a small elephant, he locked the gates again, and looked through the little barred window into The Bower of Bliss New Town where he could see the Elderly Stranger and faintly hear his/her call of...
Punk:	New soap for old! New soap for old!
Storyteller:	Enter the younger generation, led by Dick and Clappum Common twins of Tom and Harriet you met in the first half... who remembered nothing of the old days when this Freebie Soap first came to The Bower of Bliss under a different but equally appealing name.
MUSIC	*(**Generation Gap** plays as The Youngies enter differentiated from the Everyday Folk – who do not appear with them in this scene – by costume.)*
Dick:	Elderly Stranger... over here! I'll have some.
Clappum:	And me.
Storyteller:	Soon... *(Introducing each of them, as their names are stated)*... Quick, Kick and Slick were running towards the Elderly Stranger with their arms outstretched.
Quick:	And me.
Kick:	And me.

Slick: And me.

Storyteller: Before long all the Everyday Youths were clutching their so called bargain.

Youngies: Freebie Soap. Cool!

Storyteller: The Elderly Stranger happily collected their used bars of Shamay in a plastic bag secreted inside his/her mystical cloak. As (s)he gave them this soap (s)he was heard by some to say:

Punk: Be ye sure not to over-wash with this Freebie Soap lest ye...

Storyteller: But so eager were the Everyday Youngsters of The Bower of Bliss New Town to receive their gift...

All: Cool! We've got some free soap!

Storyteller: ... that they never heard the stranger's important final word.

All: *(To Storyteller.)* Well? What was it?

Storyteller: They never heard the final word.

All: Please yourself then! *(They exit.)*

Storyteller: They washed and, after a few token elephant impressions, became happier than before. Thus the Wacky Soap came once again to The Bower of Bliss New Town... to the children of those whose lives were once so tragically affected. And the song their parents once sang was cleverly re-worked for them to sing...

SONG 11: **WASH YOUR BODY**
("CELEBRATION SCRUB" REPRISE)

All:

We're all in love with these Freebie Soap packs
Mail order, E-mail or order them by fax
Come home from school and soap
away our sweat
This feeling's so appealing and it's
one I won't forget

Refrain:

We'll rub-a-dubba dub and we'll regularly scrub
All the rub-dubba dirt away
We'll hey-diddle-diddle with a grin and a giggle
As we rub-a-dub our diddles each day!
Wash your body... wash your body...
wash your body clean.
Wash your body... wash your body...
hit that washing scene.
Wash your body... wash your body clean.

Storyteller: Every week the Elderly Stranger would arrive with his familiar call.

Punk: New soap for old! New soap for old!

Storyteller: Or was it so familiar? King Huff, who had not met the stranger, listened carefully one day from within the palace walls, and realised that a letter had been added to the final word of his call:

Punk: New soap for gold! New soap for gold!

King: The stranger in the square trumpets
'New soap for gold'...
For sure my Wacky Soap here is being sold.
Do they not remember how it caused such a row?
And our dear Symbol turned to dust
Why did I their painèd memories trust?

Queen: I'm sure they remember well King Huff.
Perhaps they're flushing all this stuff
Down the loo.

King: ... I doubt that's true!
Freedom of choice my dear we pride ourselves on that. And, as I've said before, it's the price I pay for being a democrat!
Wacky Soap, I fear, is here to stay.

King & Queen: Oi, Storyteller! What do the Everyday Folk have to say?

Storyteller: Alright. *(Quick, Kick & Slick just happen to enter!)*
You! Everyday Youths.

Dick & Clappum: Who us?

Storyteller: Yes. *(Moving onto the acting area and becoming a vox pop interviewer complete with microphone.)* What's your opinion of this new Freebie Soap?

Dick & Clappum: Cool! We won't be using Shamay again... Shamay ain't hip no more!

Storyteller: Doesn't it remind you of the stories your parents tell of King Huff's Wacky Soap?

Dick: We never listen to our parents, do we Clappum?

Clappum: No Dick... our parents always exaggerate!

Storyteller: Thank-you young Everyday Folk... that'll be all.

Dick & Clappum: Cool!

Dick: *(To Clappum other as they exit.)* Wasn't that the Storyteller?

Clappum: No, the Storyteller doesn't have a mike! Anyway what would he be doing here in The Bower of Bliss New Town?

Dick & Clappum: Looking for Freebie Soap perhaps! *(They laugh!)* Cool!

Storyteller: *(Back in position.)* Wacky Soap had returned and for the most part it did make the Young Folk happy. But it caused great arguments with their parents.

Tom & Harriet: It is dangerous!

Dick & Clappum: It's fun!

Tom & Harriet: It is dangerous!

Dick & Clappum: It's fun!

Tom & Harriet: It is dangerous!

Dick & Clappum: It's fun!

Tom & Harriet: Well you're not using it in our house when you're living with us. It's like living with an elephant... all this mess!

Storyteller: All the problems were so predictable.

Tom & Harriet: *(Dick & Clappum turn... Dick has now "lost" his head and Clappum has lost her right arm.)*
Clappum Common!... What's happened to your arm... and Dick... your head!

Clappum: We're so sorry... we should have listened to you!

Storyteller: But for some... matters were much more serious... those who used Freebie Soap excessively washed themselves clean away... never to return.
Then one day the Elderly Stranger arrived at The Bower of Bliss New Town, and was to his surprise greeted by... King Huff.

Punk: *(Entering)* New soap for gold! New soap for gold!

King: Elderly Stranger, pin your ears back... hear what I've to say.
Pack up your soap and be on your way.

Punk: Pray... tell me who thou be, wearing that ridiculous costume?

King: I am King Huff!

Punk: Well thou can get stuffed!

King: You can say what you want but I have a plan
That will I am sure... stop your 'Freebie' Soap scam.

Punk: Plan away you Ridiculous Rhyming Regent.

Storyteller: The Everyday Folk with the younger generation were called before their King.

King: Bower of Bliss... Before you stands this story's 'knave'
An out and out badd'un who'll never behave
Pleadings and warnings (s)he's determined to ignore
So I have acted swiftly to settle the score
Selling Wacky Soap to the young, I cannot stop
But I can ban water... each and every drop.
Without water the lather will abate
If the young won't give the soap up...
You will all dehydrate.
(The crowd gasp.) A drought by royal command will

only be reversed
When all the soap is cast away... so... who will be the first?

Storyteller: There was silence in The Bower of Bliss New Town.

King: Have it your own way... The Bower of Bliss will from now be dry.
King Huff is a Regent you shall not defy!

Storyteller: And with that... King Huff waltzed off with his Queen.

MUSIC **SCHMALTZY HAPPY ENDING WALTZ**

(King Huff and his Queen dance offstage in a lively and absurdly inappropriate dance.)

All: A ban on water? He can't!

Oldies: This is your fault... Youngies!

Youngies: Ours?

Oldies: You're the ones using the soap.

Youngies: You used it!

Oldies: That's irrelevant.

Youngies: No it's not!

Oldies: Yes it is!

Youngies: Why is everything always our fault?

Think: Because everything always is your fault.

Youngies: You're just too old!

Oldies: And you're... *(They can't think of anything derogatory!!!)*

Youngies: We're cool!

Storyteller: The battle of the generations. *(Music starts.)*
Cue for a song?

SONG 12: **G. GAP**

Oldies:

Tidy your room and eat up your greens
Take out books from the library
That's the way to grow up good
Pop goes your childhood!

Youngies:

Why are they always moaning ...
Telling us what to do?
If having no fun means growing up good
Pop goes our childhood!

All:

We're all trapped in the generation gap
Not prepared to budge so we get into a scrap
Accused... abused... everything's unfair
In a gruesome twosome... nightmare

All:

G. gap... G. gap... do the generation gap
Do this... do that... do the generation gap
Fam'ly dynamite... ignite generation fight

Youngies: **Guilt trip... G. trip...**

Oldies: **Spoil the child and spare the whip**

All: **Just to paraphrase...**
There's not too much in them
(They point to each other) **to praise**
Blissful Bower?... Fight for Generation Power!
Do this... do that... do the generation gap.
G. gap... G. gap... Scrap scrap scrap!!!

(They fight)

Tom: Stop!!!

(They all stop fighting.)

All: Why are we blaming each other?... *(Looking and pointing at Punk.)* It's him(her) who's to blame...

Punk: Me?

All: Yes. *(They chase/threaten Punk. In the staging it would be excellent if some comic "cartoon violence" could ensue before they finally bring him/her to his/her knees and pull his/her disguise off. This could be accompanied by:)*

MUSIC:	**SILENT MOVIE THEME**
Punk:	Aaaaaaaaargh!
Tom:	Well, well well, well, well!
Harriet:	Look who it is!
All:	I don't believe it... it's Punk.
Punk:	I said I'd be back.
Tom:	This town ain't big enough for the both of us.
Punk:	Hasta la vista baby.
Tom:	Make my day Punk!
Storyteller:	Punk had met his/her match.
Tom:	A dual... to the death.
Punk:	Actually after due consideration and... well I think I'll just take the "quietly exit" option... if... if that's alright with you. *(Exits with embarrassment. Turns and says the following in a mock Austrian accent.)* I'll be back!
Tom:	That's the last we'll see of him!
Dick & Clappum:	Dad... you're a hero.
Tom:	Clappum... your arm!
Clappum:	Yes?
Tom:	It's back!!!
Clappum:	So it is! Yeh!!!
Tom & Harriet:	Dick... your head!
Dick:	Yeh?
Tom & Clappum:	It's back!!!
Dick:	So it is! Yeh!!!
Dick & Clappum:	We've learnt our lesson... we'll never use Freebie Soap again.
Clappum:	Thank-you dad, for rescuing us.

Harriet: It wasn't a very sensible thing to do! You could've had all of us killed... but... you were really brave... I do love you!

Dick & Clappum: Let's hear it, young and old alike... for Tom Common... the best dad in The Bower of Bliss New Town... *(Everyone cheers.)*

Storyteller: Finally the Generations had came together to confront a common enemy. So, just for old times sake they sang a reprise of the song which has now, in The Bower of Bliss New Town become almost redundant.

SONG 13 **G. GAP (REPRISE)**

All:

We were trapped in the generation gap
Now we've made it up so we have no need to scrap
Accused... abused... We were so unfair
In our gruesome twosome... nightmare

G. gap... G. gap... did the generation gap
Youngies: **Did this... did that... did the generation gap**
All: **Fam'ly dynamite... generations all unite**
Oldies: **Scrap the G. gap... Cuddle on your parents lap**
All: **Just to paraphrase... family unit's our new craze**

Blissful Bower... No more generation Power
Did this... did that... did the generation gap.
No more... G. gap... It's scrapped!

(They end the song in a very "cheesy" pose. "GENERATIONS UNITED!")

Storyteller: So with generations united like never before and Punk, the Baddie, banished from The Bower of Bliss New Town... things were looking distinctly 'up'. Fired with his own success the King made an announcement.

King: This time I have absolutely no doubt
Wacky Soap is gone for good... cancel the drought.

Storyteller: And without any more ado the Everyday Plumbers switched the water on again.

All: Hooray!!!

Storyteller: And that would have been that... if it wasn't for mail order and the Internet. Yes, there were still some in The Bower of Bliss New Town who could not resist the temptation of the Wacky Soap and continued to use it.

Queen: Switch off the water again!

King: Repeating the drought is not the way ahead
Our subjects must learn to think for themselves instead
We must equip them with everything they need to know
And arm them with the self-confidence to just say "no"!

Storyteller: King Huff feared for his Kingdom and remembered the promise he had made just ten years before.

King: We'll open a fund in our dear daughters name...
To pay for repairs and then to proclaim...
World-wide, the truth of Wacky Soap, and the harm it can do...
To people such as me or you.

Storyteller: King Huff's shares in the profits were still pouring in, faster than ever, but now that the repairs were completed, *(ahead of time because this is a fable)* he found he had plenty of money left over. King Huff suddenly had an idea, and without delay he E-mailed an Artist.

King: *(Busy at a computer)*
Artist in Residence with your Savoir faire...
Please would you decorate our Market Square...
A statue of our Princess is what I'd like...
Bold and beautiful, very life like...

Storyteller: *(Enter Artist.)* The artist set to work designing a Statue *(Princess Symbol is sculpted into position.)* which bore an uncanny resemblance to the real Princess Symbol. King Huff was so delighted that he decided that there should be an appealing gimmick on this monument.

Artist: Oh no it'll spoil it! Storyteller! Can't you stop him?

Storyteller: Hear him out!

King: Now add a trunk to her face, which when pulled down...
Will make the Princess frown...
And say:

Princess Symbol: Beware: Lasting happiness comes from within...
Not from a lather on your skin.

Artist: *(Melodramatically.)* This ridiculous "gimmick" cheapens my art! I want nothing to do with it! *(S/he makes to exit... with a flourish.)*

Storyteller: King Huff immediately offered the poor artist lots and lots of money.

Artist: And lots?

Storyteller: Yes! Lots and lots and lots!!!

Artist: Oh thank-you King Huff. I'm sorry about the tantrum... and if you ever have anything else to commission... here's my card. *(The Artist sculpts Symbols arm into a trunk-like position and exits. King Huff tears the card up and casts it aside.)*

Storyteller: King Huff called his Queen to show her the statue.

King: *(As the Queen enters.)* A reminder of Symbol... that should do the trick.

Queen: I'm not so sure... our Everyday Folk are all so thick!

Storyteller: The King pulled down the trunk... and to his great surprise... the statue began to sing... and dance!

SONG 14: LASTING HAPPINESS COMES FROM WITHIN

Symbol:

Lasting Happiness comes from within
Not from a quick fix lather on your skin
Use your judgement... be more shrewd
Don't use anything to change your mood

Massage your body with Wacky Soap and you...
Won't wash away depression... flush it

down the loo!
You'll smile for a while but soon it will be gone
Then you'd kill to get a bit more soap
to lather on.
So you go and get some soap... have a
show'r and smooth it on
Then look down... something's gone
End of convenient quick fix glee
As you wash away your anatomy!

All: **Lasting Happiness comes from within...**

Symbol: **Massage your body with Wacky Soap**
and you...
Won't wash away depression...
All: **Flush it down the loo!**
Symbol: **You'll smile for a while but soon it will be gone**
Join with me to spread the message of this song
All: **This soap hides a big surprise,**
You could dematerialise
Statistics lost before our eyes
Don't be fooled by a friendly name
Product danger is just the same

Lasting Happiness comes from within...

Storyteller: The Everyday Folk of The Bower of Bliss New Town passed the statue every single day, but each reacted in their own individual way.
There were those stood by the statue, dirty, smelly and very unhygenic, preaching to others as they walked by:

Squeak, Legless, Headless *(with all limbs in place)*: We advise you all never to wash.

Squeak: We haven't washed for two whole calendars.
We're dirty and we're smelly

Squeak, Legless, Headless: <u>And</u> we're proud of it!

Storyteller: They learnt the words to the statue's song and sang

	it whenever they could. *(They quietly sing the song under the following lines.)* There were those who washed but never used Wacky Soap:
The Inks:	We're still happy!
Storyteller:	There were those who ridiculed King Huff, *(Hunk flicks the "V" sign at the statue)* and scorned the statue, as they stood by the surrounding fountains, washing bits of themselves away with the Wacky Soap... just to show off to their friends.
Two Rebels:	We're their friends and we're really impressed by how anarchic they are!
Storyteller:	And there were those who, disregarding all the warnings, washed themselves clean away, never to be seen again. King Huff knew that although he was the King of a whimsical Kingdom, the happy ending he longed for so much, was not the way all stories end. He had little power over the ending. It would be decided by those, who, day after day, night after night, passed that symbolic statue in The Bower of Bliss New Town market square. King Huff's smile faded. He could not live his people's lives for them. He realised that unless his people did heed the Princess Symbol's warning, his invention could wash the happy ending clean away. Happy ever after... I wonder?
King:	Isn't there anything you can do? People like Happy endings... *(To Storyteller)*... Don't you?
Storyteller:	That isn't how I see it!
King:	Couldn't we tag something on at the end So that we can send...
All:	*(Entering)* Everyone home happily.
Storyteller:	But it isn't that kind of story... I won't give you happy endings just because you want them.

Tom:	Well then, you've left us no choice. We don't want you to write us any more. You're sacked.
Storyteller:	You can't do that to me!
All:	Oh yes we can!
Storyteller:	Oh no you can't.
All:	Oh yes we can!
Storyteller:	Oh no you can't.
All:	Oh yes we can!
Storyteller:	Oh no you can't! Suddenly a thunderstorm erupted and the Everyday Folk scattered to their sweet little homes.
Tom:	I don't hear any thunder.
Harriet:	Nor do I!
Think:	Nor me!
All:	It's such lovely weather! Isn't the sunshine wonderful?
Storyteller:	But it's raining.
All:	Oh no it's not!
Old (Wo)Man:	It's so hot I think we should all have water fights! *(A number of the cast shoot the audience, the Storyteller, and each other with water pistols.)*
Kink:	It's so hot I think we should all take our clothes off and have a celebration wash... *(They immediately start (to mime!) taking their clothes off and climbing into the showers etc.)*
Tom:	And we'll all be using...
All:	Shamay!
Storyteller:	I'll give you one final chance!
All:	*(Shouting and pointing at the Storyteller.)* Naff off! *(Those with water pistols shoot relentlessly at the Storyteller.)*

Storyteller: *(Packing up his/her things.)* Your ending fails entirely to put up a mirror to contemporary society!

All: Who gives a damn?

Storyteller: Ok I'll go...

All: Good!

Storyteller: You can keep your Happy Endings... but answer me this... what relevance do they have?

Dick: *(Impersonating)* What relevance do they have?...

Storyteller: *(As s/he leaves.)* Banal... simplistic...
they'll never learn.

Tom: Hey! Look, none of us have got any clothes on...

All: What do we care?

King: Now's our chance to invent our own happy ending...

Kink: Even if it doesn't "mirror contemporary Society"!

King & Queen: Come on! Let's sing it to make it even more climatic! *(Everyone cheers.)*

SONG 15: (SCHMALTZY) HAPPY ENDING WALTZ

(As they sing the song, the Storyteller retreats to the back of stage to collect a small suitcase. He moves forward to his storytelling position and packs his things. During the final refrain (s)he makes his/her way out of the Theatre crossing in front of the cast who ignore him/her. Storyteller waves sadly to the audience and leaves the auditorium.)

All:

Everyone's now learnt this lesson ...
"Happiness comes from within"
Everyone's acting responsibly ...
Wacky Soap won't touch our skin!

No-one is being a rebel... everyone does
what they should
All those who washed themselves
clean away... will doubtless return... if we

keep being good!
(So we'll keep being good!!!)

Ha-ppy end-ings...
Climatic music... bringing tears into your eyes
Ha-ppy endings...
So full of feeling you'll reach up for the skies!
Baddie's beat goodies... Miss becomes Mrs.
Walks into sunsets... lingering kisses
All of these elements, merge to create
The happiest ending prepared on a plate
Happy ending, schmaltzy ending,
Happy, schmaltzy, happy ending waltz.

Here's our alternative ending...
We'll have all those washed away
Reunited with all their friends...
What a wonderful day!
The King and the Queen can't see Symbol...
They've taken her loss oh so hard
Suddenly Symbol appears in white...

Symbol: I'm going to marry the infamous Silly Guard!

All: (No not the Silly Guard!)

Ha-ppy end-ings...
Climatic music... bringing tears into your eyes
Ha-ppy endings...
So full of feeling you'll reach up for the skies!
Baddie's beat goodies... Miss becomes Mrs.
Walks into sunsets... lingering kisses
All of these elements, merge to create
The happiest ending prepared on a plate
Happy ending, schmaltzy ending,
Happy, schmaltzy, happy ending waltz.
Schmaltzy happy... schmaltzy ending...
happy ending Waltz.

SONG 16: WASH YOUR BODY (REPRISE)

All:

We're back in love with our Shamay Soap bars
Ripping off our clothes to wash
beneath the stars
Public washing... we're always very keen
Fully understanding that this soap will only clean!

Refrain:

All:

We'll rub-a-dubba dub and we'll regularly scrub
All the rub-dubba dirt away
We'll hey-diddle-diddle with a grin and a giggle
As we rub-a-dub our diddles each day!
Wash your body... wash your body...
wash your body clean.
Wash your body... wash your body...
hit that washing scene.
Wash your body... wash your body clean.

SONG 17: LASTING HAPPINESS COMES FROM WITHIN

Symbol:

Lasting Happiness comes from within
Not from a quick fix lather on your skin
Use your judgement... be more shrewd
Don't use anything to change your mood

All:

Massage your body with Wacky Soap
and you...
Won't wash away depression...
flush it down the loo!
You'll smile for a while but soon it will be gone
Then you'd kill to get a bit more soap
to lather on.
So you go and get some soap,
have a show'r and smooth it on
Then look down... something's gone
End of convenient quick fix glee
As you wash away your anatomy!

Lasting Happiness comes from within...

Symbol: Massage your body with Wacky Soap
and you...
Won't wash away depression...

All: Flush it down the loo!

Symbol: You'll smile for a while but soon it will be gone
Join with me to spread the message of this song
This soap hides a big surprise,
you could demater'alise
Statistics lost right before our eyes
Don't be fooled by a friendly name
Product danger is just the same

Lasting Happiness comes from within...

THE END

Follow up Work

(Key Stage 3/4 Drama/English/PSHE. Also opportunities for links with Art/Music.)

IMPROVISATION:

The following improvisations may be conducted by either:-

a. Class working in small groups simultaneously with no-one watching so that all can have the experience of "doing" at first hand.

b. Volunteer groups who perform **spontaneously** in front of the class. This 'performance' can then be used as a common reference point for class discussion. The inclusion of a teacher-chaired discussion is crucial to the success of these activities.

A discussion prior to any of these activities can establish the government's stance on Wacky Soap. Is it to be legal? Are there any age restrictions... or any other restrictions? This can obviously be done in or out of role. Alternatively rules can be invented (and subsequently revoked), where appropriate, to enable maximum experimentation with ideas.

Group work; exploration of issues; (role?)

1. *Parent/Son or Daughter.*

Whilst tidying his/her son/daughter's room a parent discovers a bar of Wacky Soap hidden away in a drawer. Later that day the son/daughter arrives home form school. What does the parent say?

This improvisation can be repeated with the parent or son/daughter having a different attitude or reason for having the soap in the drawer which could be written on a card and given to the improviser prior to starting the scene. e.g. You stole the bar of Wacky Soap and have not used it yet... you have been given the bar of Wacky Soap and used it once last night... a friend has asked you to/made you look after it for them. or as a parent... you never use Wacky Soap... you are a casual Wacky Soap user... you used Wacky soap when you were younger and your son/daughter doesn't know... you used it when you were younger and your best friend disappeared.

Role; Appropriate use of Language; Exploration of issues.

2. *Parent/Son or Daughter.*

Son/Daughter returns home from a teenagers party where Wacky Soap had been used. His/Her right hand/arm is, as a consequence of overuse, temporarily missing! The student playing the son/daughter

should work with one empty sleeve representing the missing arm. On arrival at home the parents notice. How do they deal with this?

Role; Appropriate use of Language; Exploration of issues.

3. *Parent/Son or Daughter.*

Will the parents send their son/daughter into school the following morning if their hand/arm has not returned? This could be discussed over breakfast. The stakes could be heightened in a repeated scene by saying that on this morning an external SATS/GCSE exam was to occur.

Role; Appropriate use of Language; Exploration of issues.

4. *Head teacher/student.*

How should a Head teacher react if the son/daughter does arrive at school with an arm missing... clearly an outward show of Wacky Soap use. The scene could begin with the Head teacher seeing the student on the way to his/her classroom.

Role; Appropriate use of Language; Exploration of issues.

5. *Parent/Son or Daughter.*

Would the parents allow their son/daughter to go to, or even take Wacky Soap to such a party in the future... clearly this will be influenced to a large extent by legalities established in the opening discussion... but it is interesting to try the scene out with it being legal in the first instance and then with it being illegal.

Role; Appropriate use of Language; Exploration of issues.

6. *Parent/Son or Daughter.*

Would the parents be prepared to buy 20-30 bars of Wacky Soap for son/daughter's 16th birthday party to be held in their house, (working in the scenario of, for example, Wacky Soap being legal for over 16's). Bear in mind the parents may well always use Wacky Soap themselves on special occasions. Even if they don't the son/daughter requesting permission is an even more challenging scene.

Role; Appropriate use of Language; Exploration of issues.

7. Evaluation of the activity focusing on individual work... content, and issues raised.

Exploration of issues; Evaluation.

SMALL GROUP PLAY MAKING:

In small groups (self selected, but not leaving anyone out) devise either:

a. A Wacky Soap advert to promote the product. This could be a poster campaign (tableaux), for the less able/confident or a one minute 'short'. **It is important to limit time to one minute!** This presentation should include plenty of ***choral speaking*** and should pastiche current advert styles... the teacher might get the class to talk about adverts before they begin work. **Songs** (Jingles) and **rhyme** may be appropriate. Sometimes there have been opportunities for cross curricular links with **Music** on this.

b. A Health Education campaign to warn people of the dangers of Wacky Soap. Examples of such campaigns would be useful to discuss at this point. Again this presentation should include plenty of ***choral speaking*** and should pastiche current Health Education 'warning' styles. **Songs** (Jingles) and **rhyme** may be appropriate.

Group work (during rehearsal period); Role; Appropriate use of Language, Movement & Space (during presentation); Evaluation (after performance). (There are obvious cross curricular opportunities with the Art Department: poster designing and pictures of events depicted in the story, and of the soap itself).

WHOLE CLASS IMPROVISATION:

1. Whole class in a meeting at a local community centre debating the proposal that a new Wacky Soap factory should be built on vacant council land which is in the same road as the local Junior school, Secondary school and Youth Club. The factory will bring in much needed income to the town through rent, new employment etc. However, a national protest group *Action Against Wacky Soap* has been formed to try to ban Wacky Soap.

Wacky Soap Incorporates are aware of their controversial nature and are prepared to provide some kind of facility for the community... such as an Ice Rink etc. They may also be keen to 'sponsor' a classroom in the school. They are planning to produce their own Health Education pack detailing the dangers of Wacky Soap and a guide to using Wacky Soap safely. This will be provided free to schools.

Many jobs will be provided for the local community. If the factory is not built here there are already plans for it to be built elsewhere.

In a typical class of 30, parts could be allocated thus:

1 Chair – possibly the teacher.

4 members of *The Wacky Soap Users Group* all of whom use Wacky Soap regularly as part of their family life.

1 Managing Director of *Wacky Soap Inc.*

1 Manager(ess) of the only other existing Wacky Soap factory in a similar community in the Midlands. He/She has first hand experience of establishing such a venture with success.

1 person appointed to become the new factory manager(ess) and who is responsible for appointing new staff (from the local community).

2 Head teachers – one from the Junior and one form the Secondary School.

2 Deputy Heads... responsible for Pupil welfare.

1 Youth club leader.

4 Town Councillors.

2 local Police Officers.

5 members of *Action Against Wacky Soap.*

Prior to the meeting each sub-group should meet to decide attitude to the proposal and, perhaps, meet up with other like minded sub-groups.

Group work; Role; Exploration of issues.

2. The teachers may suggest a scenario where the locals refuse to work in such a factory and could then through active role play, explore the relationships between workers drafted in from elsewhere and the locals. There may be a small number of locals who do choose to accept a job at the factory. There are obvious parallels to draw with this to provoke further discussion.

Role; Appropriate use of Language; Exploration of issues.

3. A delegation of workers (the majority of the class) arrive to see the management team (students in role) about anxieties over a colleague who is beginning to abuse Wacky Soap and is, in their view, in danger of

a. disappearing

b. causing an accident at work due to an increasing deficit of limbs!

Role; Appropriate use of Language; Exploration of issues.

What is the responsibility of the management team? Should the colleague be sacked or assisted by the company? Should the contracts be written in such a way as to imply a specific management attitude to the workforce's use of Wacky Soap? If so... what are the implications of that?

Ongoing evaluation.

These questions should be fed into the role-play by the teacher who can be either in role or observing and freezing from the side.

Presentation:

4. How do Wacky Soap Incorporates cope with the news that a media figure (pop star, footballer, MP, Royal Family member) has disappeared. The reason for the disappearance is claimed to be Wacky Soap abuse. Devise and present a 2-minute news item telling of the above including:

- **(i)** information about the celebrity, his/her "battle" with Wacky Soap
- **(ii)** interviews with family/friends and fans
- **(iii)** interviews with AAWS representative
- **(iii)** interviews with WSI.

Role; Appropriate use of Language, Movement and Space; Exploration of issues.

If you have enjoyed reading and/or working with this playscript, you may like to find out about other plays we publish. There are brief descriptions and other details on the following pages.

All plays deal with contemporary social and moral issues and are suitable for Youth Theatres, Schools, Colleges, and adult AmDram. They are ideal for GCSE Drama/English exam use and frequently do well in One Act Play Festivals. They offer both male and female performers equally challenging opportunities.

For enquiries or to order plays published by *dbda*, please contact:
dbda, Pin Point, Rosslyn Crescent, Harrow HA1 2SB.
Tel: 0870 333 7771
Fax: 0870 333 7772
E-mail: info@dbda.co.uk

All enquiries regarding performing rights of plays by *Mark Wheeller*, should be made to:
Sophie Gorel Barnes, MBA Literary Agents,
62 Grafton Way, London W1P 5LD.
Tel: 020 7387 2076
E-mail: sophie@mbalit.co.uk

All enquiries regarding performing rights of 'Heroin Lies' by *Wayne Denfhy*, should be made to:
Wayne Denfhy, c/o ***dbda***,
Pin Point, Rosslyn Crescent, Harrow HA1 2SB.
Tel: 0870 333 7771
E-mail: info@dbda.co.uk (subject: Wayne Denfhy)

All enquiries regarding performing rights of 'Gagging For It' by *Danny Sturrock*, should be made to:
Danny Sturrock, c/o ***dbda***,
Pin Point, Rosslyn Crescent, Harrow HA1 2SB.
Tel: 0870 333 7771
E-mail: info@dbda.co.uk (subject: Danny Sturrock)

Other plays published by *dbda*

Wacky Soap – *a Musical with a difference...*

Wacky Soap is a Pythonesque allegorical tale about 'substance' abuse (drugs, alcohol, glue, tobacco, etc). While washing with Wacky Soap leads to instant happiness and an inclination towards outrageous behaviour, prolonged use washes away limbs and ultimately leads to dematerialisation. This has become a tried and tested (and increasingly popular) School/ Drama Club/Youth Theatre production and is an ideal vehicle for a cast of any age.

The story of Wacky Soap, by Mark Wheeler, first appeared as a full **Musical play.** The play script of the full version (shown below) includes scheme of work for KS3/4. A mini version of the play is included with the **Music Score**.

ISBN 1 902843 02 9
KS 3/4 to adult

Wacky Soap – A Cautionary Tale by Mark Wheeler

Cast: *6-100!*

Duration: *50 mins play / 80 mins musical*

'This (play) gave every member of the large and energetic cast opportunities to shine... King Huff addressed his subjects from a Bouncy Castle, just one of the touches of visual humour in this fast, funny and thought provoking evening.'

Barbara Hart, Southern Evening Echo
Curtain Call Nominated "Best Production 2000"

ISBN 1 902843 06 1
KS 2&3

Wacky Soap – The Music Score and Mini Musical
by Mark Wheeler and James Holmes

Mini-Musical Duration: *40 mins*

A **Past-performance CD** gives you the opportunity to hear the songs of the play, while a fully orchestrated **Backing track CD** will be invaluable to those who want to produce the play but do not have music facilities.

"Wacky Soap was an outstanding success!!!... We have had letters from people in the audience saying what a fab show it was and how impressed they were.

The most frequent comment was that it was a 'risk' to put it on as a school show (as opposed to doing 'Oliver' or 'Little Shop of Horrors') and one that thoroughly paid off!! 'The feel good factor was amazing' was another comment we had.

Many people said how impressed they were by the 'community' spirit of the production – everybody working together without the 'star' element creeping in!"

John Plant, Head of Drama, Southmoor School, Sunderland

The Story of Wacky Soap
by Mark & Rachel Wheeller
Illustrations by Geoffrey Greiggs

ISBN 1 902843 07 X

A beautifully illustrated book with the story of Wacky Soap in prose form.
It is often used as inspiration with props and costumes for when producing the play.

ISBN 1 902843 17 1

Cast: *3f, 3m &3m/f or 3m & 3f for GCSE using suggested cuts*
Duration: *55 minutes approx.*
KS 3 & 4

NEW – Gagging for it by Danny Sturrock

Summer is here, A-levels are over and a group of 6 friends embark on a holiday to Ibiza! What would their holiday bring? Would Chris finally pluck up the courage to ask out Teresa? Would Jay drink himself into oblivion? Would Bianca spend the entire holiday flirting with the Spanish barmen – more than likely! ...or would a chance encounter with an old friend bring their hedonistic worlds crashing down around them!?

Comedy, dance music and choreography are the keys to this production. The pace is breakneck and hilarious, but once the party's over, it hits you!

'Really funny... laugh out loud funny. Inspired outstanding performances from the six Year 11s who went on to exceed our expectations by a long way in their GCSEs achieving A or A*. It proved to be a firm favourite with our KS3/4 audience.'

Mark Wheeller

ISBN 1 902843 18 5

Cast: *2f & 2m with doubling*
Duration: *60 minutes approx.*
KS 3 & 4 and A Level

NEW – Legal Weapon II by Mark Wheeller

This is a new "improved" version of the popular Legal Weapon play which, from summer 2005, will go out on tour to schools across the UK.

Legal Weapon told the story of a young man's relationship with his girlfriend, Jazz, and his car. Both are flawed, but his speeding causes the loss of a life and the loss of his freedom.

In Legal Weapon II Andy has to reveal to Jazz that he has killed someone very close to her... her best friend!

Legal Weapon was once described as "fast, funny and very powerful".

Legal Weapon II promises to be faster, funnier and far more powerful!

ISBN 1 902843 14 2

Cast: 2f & 2m with doubling, or up to 30
Duration: 70 minutes approx.
KS 3 & 4

The Gate Escape by Mark Wheeller

The story of two truants. Corey is 'addicted' to bunking school. Chalkie views himself as a casual truant "no problem!" While truanting with some friends, the pair are greeted by a surreal 'Big Brother' figure who sets them a task. The loser will be in for some dramatic 'Big Bother'... Who will lose?... What will this 'bother' be?

The play has toured professionally in Hampshire in 2003, to great acclaim.

'A lively dramatic style and innovative structure with dynamic and contemporary dialogue. It is written in a way to guarantee that the audience will feel fully involved and enthralled by the main characters.'

Professor Ken Reid, Author of Tackling Truancy in Schools

'I loved the piece – it really was Mark Wheeller at his absolute best... I loved so many of the ideas... inspired.'

Neil Phillips, Head of Drama and Edexcel GCSE Examiner

ISBN 1 902843 15 0

Cast: 8f, 7m and 2m/f
Duration: 70 minutes approx.
KS 3 & 4

Heroin Lies by Wayne Denfhy

A sensitive, yet disturbing look at drugs and drug dependency, in particular the pressures and influences at play on an ordinary teenage girl. We observe Vicki's gradual and tragic slide towards addiction and also the various degrees of help and hindrance she receives from family and friends.

This is a new, updated edition of Wayne Denfhy's popular play. It is suitable for performance as well as for reading in the class. Included with the playscript is an excellent scheme for follow-up work by Peter Rowlands.

'...a piece of drama that will stimulate and challenge a young cast... Heroin Lies deals with vital issues that affect today's youngsters in a gentle and humane way and, in so doing, gets its message across without the instant rejection that can meet other approaches.'

Pete Sanpher, Head of Drama, Norfolk

Other plays published by ***dbda***

ISBN 1 902843 05 3

Cast: *2f & 2m with doubling or 3f, 3m & 6*
Duration: *50 minutes approx.*
KS 4 to adult

Too Much Punch for Judy by Mark Wheeller

A hard-hitting documentary play, based on a tragic drink-drive accident that results in the death of Jo, front seat passenger. The driver, her sister Judy, escapes unhurt (or has she?).

The tragic incident was dramatised by Mark in 1986 using only the words of those most closely involved and affected. This play has become one of the most frequently performed plays ever!

'The play will have an impact on young people or adults. It will provoke discussion. It stimulates and wants you to cry out for immediate social action and resolution.'

Henry Shankula – Addiction Research Foundation, Toronto

'The young audience I was sat in was patently out for some whooping Friday night fun... at the end there was a horrid silence.'

Nick Baker – Times Educational Supplement

ISBN 1 902843 00 2

KS 3 & 4

Why did the chicken cross the road? by Mark Wheeller

Cast: *2m & 2f with doubling, or 3f, 3m & 3*

Duration: *35 minutes*

The story of two cousins, Tammy and Chris. Tammy gets killed in a stupid game of 'chicken' on the one morning that the cousins do not cycle to school. Chris, unable to tell anyone else about his part in the accident, has to live with this dreadful secret.

'An imaginative and moving look at risk taking at a time when peer pressure is at its strongest.'

Rosie Welch, LARSOA

ISBN 1 902843 08 8

KS 3 to adult

Hard to Swallow by Mark Wheeller

Cast: *3f & 2m with doubling, or 6f, 3m & 16*

Duration: *70 minutes*

This play is an adaptation of Maureen Dunbar's award winning book (and film) ***Catherine*** which charts her daughter's uneven battle with anorexia and the family's difficulties in coping with the illness.

'This play reaches moments of almost unbearable intensity... naturalistic scenes flow seamlessly into sequences of highly stylised theatre... such potent theatre!'

Vera Lustiq – The Independent

ISBN 1 902843 09 6

KS 3/4 to adult

GRAHAM – World's Fastest Blind Man! by Mark Wheeller

Cast: *5m & 4f with doubling, or up to 34*

Duration: *80 minutes*

A play full of lively humour telling the inspirational story of Graham Salmon MBE. Totally blind since birth, Graham went on to become the World's Fastest Blind Man running 100 metres in 11.4 seconds! The play, written in Mark's unique documentary style, skillfully brings to life Graham's courage, tenacity and wonderful sense of humour.

'Very good, very moving, very very funny!'

Bruce Henderson, Principal Teacher of Drama,
Wester Hailes Education Centre, Edinburgh

ISBN 1 902843 16 9

KS 3/4 to adult

Missing Dan Nolan (based on a true story) by Mark Wheeller

Cast: *2m & 2f with doubling, or up to 18*

Duration: *45-50 minutes*

This play, based on the true story of Dan Nolan, a teenage boy who went missing on the night of January 1st 2002, is written in the same documentary style as 'Too Much Punch for Judy'. During 2003, it has been shown at various Drama Festivals and has won awards and commendations at every one!

'Unusual and deeply affecting. Skillfully written... achieves astonishing depth and authenticity... addresses a wound still raw and stands as a fitting testament to a young life.'

Charles Evans, Adjudicator, Eastleigh Drama Festival

Mark Wheeller's

GRAHAM

World's Fastest Blind Man!

A play telling the amazing true life story of World Champion Blind Athlete Graham Salmon MBE who sadly died in 1999. It was premiered at the 2002 Edinburgh Festival Fringe.

"I came to know Graham Salmon in 1982 when, wlth Epping Youth Theatre, I wrote a play telling about his inspiring life. We became close friends. In 1998 Graham suffered an unbelievably cruel twist of fate. A malignant tumour was discovered in his leg... it had to be amputated.

Shortly afterwards my then seven year old son, Charlie, asked Graham if he would join him in a game of football. I was concerned by this request but Graham had no such worries and took Charlie outside and played football with him... taking shots with his remaining leg and, as he became tired, used his crutch and did some headers!

It is for me the most 'personal' play I think I shall ever write. Graham's life story is actually full of humour. The role of Graham provides an excellent opportunity for any actor. Most of my plays have been performed (brilliantly) by young people, adults in amateur companies and professional actors. I hope that GRAHAM will be embraced with equal enthusiasm."

Mark Wheeller

"Graham Salmon is the most inspiring athlete I have met; I say this without a moment's hesitation even though I have enjoyed the rare privilege of sharing the company of Muhammad Ali, Stanley Matthews, Gary Sobers, Martina Navratilova, Nadia Comaneci, Arnold Palmer and countless others in the course of my job."
***Robert Philip**, Daily Telegraph*

"I was really wowed by "Graham"... offered excellent opportunities for imaginative stylised performance with GCSE students... The peaks of tension and moments of pathos really moved me... I will definitely be offering 'Graham' to my classes this year.'
***Neil Phillips**, Head of Drama and Edexcel GCSE Examiner*

"Very moving, very very funny, very well performed, very good!'
***Bruce Henderson**, Principal Teacher of Drama,*
Wester Hailes Education Centre, Edinburgh

Extracts from 'Graham – World's Fastest Blind Runner'

Graham: Nothing was real to me until I'd touched it. That posed a problem... not everything I wanted to feel was easily examined by a small boy. One example, is something that sighted people take for granted... light. The best way for me to experience it was to touch it... so with the kind of precision demonstrated by the Dam busters *(Perhaps here the Dam busters music could be used and all, as aeroplanes, get into position!)*, Susan took me into our narrow hallway and lined me up underneath the lampshade hanging from the ceiling. There was little point in me touching it unless it was switched on... so...

Susan: I clicked the switch... and he was off!

Graham: With one foot on the wall I inched my way up towards the ceiling until I could feel the warmth of the bulb on my face...

Susan: ... then, like Columbus landing on America, he touched the "light".

Graham: Owwwww!

Susan: The joy of discovery was tempered by pain...

Graham: ... not just from the bulb!

Maud: His shoes had been muddy... *(Maud smacks his backside)*
... my walls had been very clean.

Graham: *(Holding his backside.)*... and my path to en"light"enment had to lie low for a few days while mum cleaned up my quest for illumination!

Roger: The sun was blazing down on Varna Stadium.

Marie: Graham and Roger climbed to the back of the stands to find some shade.

John: In 90 minutes Graham would know whether all the hard work would be rewarded.

Graham: My legs still felt sore from the previous evening's semi-finals.

Marie: He stretched out on a bench and tried to relax.

Roger: We could hear the flags flapping in the wind and a buzz of conversation amongst the competitors and the spectators.

Mark: Thoughts came flooding into Graham's mind with no rhyme nor reason. *(Possibly the cast could create still images depicting the events as they are described to animate the thoughts.)*

Maud: Unconnected incidents... like, how as a child he had ridden his bike in Woodland Street.

Marie: How in his youth he had dreamt of finding fame and fortune as a rock star.

John: His meeting with Ron Murray, and that great night at Crystal Palace when he became the first blind person to run on equal terms against sighted athletes.

Marie: On hearing that his name was to appear in ***The Guinness Book Of Records*** for his world record run.

Roger: He thought of his friends at home...

Marie: His mum and dad...

Graham: I stood up to cheer Bob Matthews home in the 1500.

Roger: Are you ready?

Other Plays by Mark Wheeller (not published by ***dbda***)

Arson About

Script: Mark Wheeller (Ed. Andy Kempe)
Duration: 75 mins
Cast: 4 (2f & 2m with doubling)
Published by: Nelson Thornes Ltd. Tel: 01242 267100

Mollie and Ian are hot for each other. Stueey can be a real bright spark. Mr Butcher's comments have inflamed Shuttle. All in all it's combustible material but when you play with fire it can be more than your fingers that get burnt. Alrson About is a theatrical power keg which crackles with wit and moves along with a scorching pace. But in this play by Mark Wheeller the cost of 'arson about' becomes all too clear.

Chunnel of Love

Script: Graham Cole & Mark Wheeller
Duration: 100 mins
Cast: 25 (11f, 8m & 6m/f)
Published by: Zig Zag Education. Tel: 0117 950 3199

A bi-lingual play (80% English & 20% French) about teenage pregnancy. Lucy is fourteen - she hopes to become a vet and is working hard to gain good grades in her GCSE exams, when she discovers she is pregnant. She faces a series of major decisions, not least of which is what to tell the father... Ideal as a school production and Key Stage 4 Drama course book.

Sweet FA !

Script: Mark Wheeller
Duration: 45 mins plus interval
Cast: 3f / 2m (or more)
Published by: SchoolPlay Productions Ltd. Tel: 01206 540111

A Zigger Zagger for girls (and boys)! A new play (also available as a full length Musical) telling the true life story of Southampton girl footballer Sarah Stanbury (Sedge) whose ambition is to play Football (Soccer) for England. Her dad is delighted ... her mum disapproves strongly! An ideal GCSE production and Key Stage 4 Drama course book. Drama GCSE scheme of work also available.

Blackout – One Evacuee in Thousands

MUSICAL

Script: Mark Wheeller with the Stantonbury Youth Theatre
Music: Mark Wheeller
Duration: 90 mins plus interval
Published by: SchoolPlay Productions Ltd.

A Musical about the plight of Rachel Eagle, a fictional evacuee in World War II. Rachel's parents are determined that the war will not split the family up. After refusing to have her evacuated in 1939 they decide to do so midway though 1940. At first Rachel does not settle but, after the death of her mother, she becomes increasingly at home with her billets in Northamptonshire. When her father requests that she return she wants to stay where she feels at home. An ideal large scale school production with good parts for girls (and boys).

The Most Absurd Xmas (Promenade?) Musical in the World... Ever!

Script: Lyndsey Adams, Michael Johnston, Stuart White & Mark Wheeller
Cast: Big!
Music: James Holmes
Duration: 100 mins
Published by: SchoolPlay Productions Ltd. Tel: 01206 540111

Eat your heart out Ionesco! If you want a musical with a message ... don't consider this one! Santa fails to arrive one year in the Bower of Bliss. Why not? A shortage of carrots perhaps? Or is it because the central character is forbidden to use her musical gift, and whose parents disguise her as a cactus? It all ends reasonably happily and is a bundle of laughs. Originally conceived as a Promenade production. An ideal large scale school Christmas production or alternative an "absurd" summer production.

For more details and an up-to-date list of plays, please visit Mark's website:
www.amdram.co.uk/wheellerplays *(please note wheeller has two "l")*